PRIVATE PILOT STUDIES

By the same authors:

GROUND STUDIES FOR PILOTS

AVIATION LAW

PRIVATE PILOT STUDIES

S. E. T. TAYLOR
formerly BOAC and Chief Ground Instructor
London School of Flying

H. A. PARMAR
formerly RAF and Specialist Instructor
London School of Flying, Chief Instructor
MAT Kuala Lumpur

Revised by
R. B. UNDERDOWN FRMetS MRAeS
formerly Director of Ground Training
and latterly Principal, College of
Air Training, Hamble, Hants.

FIFTH EDITION

T. & A. D. POYSER
Calton

Fifth edition, published by T. & A. D. Poyser Ltd,
Calton, Waterhouses, Staffordshire, England

First edition 1972
Second edition 1975
Third edition 1977
Fourth edition 1979
Fifth edition 1987

ISBN 0 85661 045 3

Text set in $9\frac{1}{2}/11$pt Linotron Melior, printed by photolithography
and bound in Great Britain at The Bath Press, Avon

Contents

Preface

The original authors (sadly both now deceased) first wrote this book to meet a demand from those studying for their written and oral examinations for the Private Pilot's Licence. In addition, other helpful matter is included and where this is not a part of the PPL syllabus this is usually stated or will be apparent to the reader. A selection of typical PPL examination questions, based on past papers and our reasonable belief that a question on such-and-such is bound to turn up sooner or later, are also included. We don't guarantee that any of our selection will actually appear in future examinations for the PPL but at least you will have some idea of the type of questions you may be asked.

The book contains a chapter on such matters as insurance, legal responsibilities, safety, etc., and although this is not exam material we believe that there are few pilots, qualified or student, who will not welcome and benefit from the information it contains. The authors wish to thank the Royal Aeronautical Society for permission to base the chapter on an article on this subject by Peter Martin LL.B., published in the *Aeronautical Journal*.

We are also grateful to David Ogilvy of the Shuttleworth Collection and BLAC for invaluable help and advice with some sections of the book, and to Brian Tighe, formerly of the London School of Flying.

It should perhaps be noted that throughout the text whole numbers of 1 000 or more appear, in line with recommended practice, with a space instead of a comma between thousands.

In revising this book to bring it up-to-date, I wish to acknowledge the ready permission of the CAA to reproduce the sections of their 1:500 000 chart and Airtour International to reproduce the navigation computer.

Hamble   Roy B. Underdown

1: Come fly with me

Of all the developments of the twentieth century, the ability to fly probably assumes the premier place insofar as changing the pattern of life for us all. International travel by air on business and on holiday has expanded out of all recognition and is now taken as commonplace. In parallel with the expansion of commercial aviation has come expansion of private flying. No longer is weekend flying the prerogative of only the well-heeled or of pilots in the reserve forces.

Now you have decided that it is time that you came flying too. Perhaps you have recently flown home after a holiday relaxing in the sun watching seagulls doing aerobatics and have a yearning to take to the air again. Whatever your motivation, this book tells you what private flying is all about and why. You will find that both the practical and theoretical work involved in becoming a pilot requires concentration, dedication and industry but its rewards are both exhilarating and satisfying. Modern private aircraft are efficient, comfortable and safe and the syllabus for a private pilot's licence is intended to ensure that aircraft are operated as efficiently and safely as possible. Flying opens up a whole new world of beauty and provides the opportunity to enjoy the experience of operating a sophisticated piece of machinery in three dimensions. It is a fascinating and glamorous pastime but for whatever reason you have decided to learn to fly, you must convince the Civil Aviation Authority you are fit enough to be responsible for handling an aeroplane. Hence the contents of this book.

The aviation system in the United Kingdom is designed as much to handle General Aviation as it is the traffic of the airlines. To start with, all aircraft are built with approved materials and their maintenance in an airworthy condition is regularly supervised and inspected. Each aeroplane is flight-tested and must be flown (including engine-handling) within laid-down parameters. The initial flying exercises for student pilots concentrate on general handling, take-offs, circuits and landings.

However, you will not spend all your time just doing circuits at your local airfield so a study of maps and charts and cross-country navigation procedures is also an essential element of your studies. Pilots use a navigation computer which solves a vector triangle to determine the aeroplane's drift, ground speed, etc. Operating in three dimensions, pilots need to know how to read the instruments giving the aeroplane's altitude, speed and direction and any corrections to the readings that these instruments require.

For both local and cross-country flying, the impact of the weather on your flight can be extremely significant. A study of basic meteorology – the science of the weather, both actual and forecast – is a must and you will be surprised how 'weather-minded' practising pilots are, not only on their flying days but in their lives generally. Given the average conditions met by a student pilot during his training, your instructor will normally be able to point out to you on your flying days the varying cloud types, weather systems and effects of varying wind directions and speeds to reinforce the meteorology theory you are studying.

The aviation system, however, only works because of the basic common-sense, courtesy and camaraderie of aviators and the legal responsibilities imposed upon anyone in charge of an aeroplane. For safe operations, pilots are constrained by aviation law, flight rules and procedures. Unlike road traffic rules for avoidance of collision where each country has its own notions as to what speeds and on which side of the road motorists must drive, aviation collision-avoidance rules are like those of the mariner – internationally common. Obviously, too, there must be international agreement on ground-to-air signals, customs procedures, etc. Importantly, too, there is the obligation also to those beneath the aircraft's flight path in both environmental and in safety terms.

The old saying 'What goes up, must come down' was around long before the Wright brothers. However, the whole process of learning to be a pilot is to enable you to go up and down enjoyably and safely. Don't be put off by the dial-twiddling, switch-flipping image of a pilot looking out of the flight deck window with half an eye on his instruments, conversing all the time on the radio. The following chapters are intended to help you unravel the mysteries and mystique of what you have seen on your demonstration flight or on the screen, while your flying instructor can concentrate on the physical aspects of enhancing hand and eye co-ordination, your judgment and general airmanship skills.

2: Principles of flight and airframes

Basically an aeroplane structure is composed of a fuselage (the technical term for the body), wings and a tail unit, while the unit known as the undercarriage or landing gear carries the wheels – these main components are shown in Fig. 2.1. However, here we are mainly concerned with those parts of the machine that exist specifically to enable it to fly. These are the wings and ailerons, tailplane and elevators, and fin and rudder, each of which will be described as we meet it.

FIG 2.1

Lift

An aeroplane flies because of the lift obtained from the wings (or main-planes as they are sometimes called), and this is provided mostly by the shape, or aerofoil section, of the wings and the actual wing surfaces. If we hold a stiffish flat card more or less horizontally and draw it fairly rapidly through the air, it will tend to rise only if it is held at a positive (or upward) angle to the direction in which it is moving. This is because the air strikes the lower surface of the angled card and so causes an increase in air pressure which creates some lift. However, this would be a most inefficient way of getting into the air, but if we can increase the pressure on the lower surface of the wing and at the same time (and more impor-tantly) decrease the pressure above it, the difference in relative pressures (push from below, suction from above) will provide a much more worth-while result.

This more efficient lift is achieved by shaping the wing to give a smooth aerofoil section which requires the air passing over the upper surface of the wing, as shown in Fig. 2.2, to travel further than that passing below. With a greater distance to travel, but with no more time in which to do it (more air is always following and 'chasing' it) the air must travel faster. Now an old master of theory named Bernoulli (the name matters little but the result is important) proved that an increase in speed of a fluid (in our case air) causes a decrease in pressure and, of course, vice versa. As a result, then, the shaped aerofoil section, reducing pressure above it, gives us greatly more lift than would be possible from a flat wing, as is shown in Fig. 2.3.

FIG 2.2

FIG 2.3

   Although the aerofoil section gives us our required lift we must be able to control the amount of life produced. For level flight the lift provided must balance the aircraft's weight, the gravitational force. There are two controlling factors that can be adjusted by the pilot – the airspeed and the angle of attack of the wings. Clearly the faster we fly through the air the more lift we will achieve, but to achieve the required amount we must be able to increase or decrease the angle at which the wings meet the oncoming airflow. This angle is known as the angle of attack and, as shown in Fig. 2.4, it is the angle measured between the direction

FIG 2.4

of the airflow and the chord line (a line drawn between the leading and trailing edges) of the wing.

Because more speed creates more lift, we reduce the angle of attack in level flight (by use of the elevators to depress the nose) as we increase speed. Conversely, as we reduce speed we increase the angle of attack in order to maintain level flight. Figure 2.5 shows the likely pressure distribution at, (a), a small angle of attack; and, (b), a larger angle.

(a)   (b)

FIG 2.5

All this makes sense and behaves itself until we reach what is known as the stalling angle, which is the critical point at which the streamlined flow of air over the wing's upper surface is obliged to change its direction too abruptly to be able to follow the wing curvature. The flow then breaks away above the wing's upper surface and introduces eddies in the hitherto streamlined airflow that was producing most of the lift, and beyond this critical angle we cannot remain in fully controlled, sustained flight. Figure 2.6(b) shows the effect on the airflow as the wing begins to meet it at the stalling angle. As the angle of attack is further increased the eddies, which formed initially towards the trailing edge of the wing, now work

(a) low angle of attack – streamlined flow

(b) high angle of attack – streamlines breaking up

FIG 2.6

towards the leading edge, depriving more and more of the wing of its lift.

Many people tend to speak of stalling speed, but although there is an airspeed at which, in straight and level flight, the stalling angle will be reached a pilot must remember that regardless of airspeed a wing will stall whenever it reaches the critical angle. It is possible (to give a more extreme example) to be diving fast, and to pull out abruptly with the result that although the attitude of the machine changes it continues temporarily on its original flight path and therefore attains the stalling angle. This situation is known as a high speed stall and maybe the average private pilot will never meet it, but there are many other possibilities (such as increased loading in a turn, as will be explained later); the pilot must be able to recognise the symptoms (airframe buffeting, or shaking of the control column) and take remedial action.

From a practical viewpoint, the main facts for the pilot to remember are that he has two variables directly under his control. The more obvious of these is airspeed and, broadly speaking, the more of this he has the safer the situation. The second variable is the angle of attack. As, at any given angle of attack, the wing will produce more lift as the airspeed increases, it follows logically that in level flight at high speed the angle of attack must be small and the aircraft's attitude is nose down. At low speeds the nose attitude is high, and this can be an indication of the approach to the stalled condition. Another symptom (apart from the buffeting already mentioned) is the sloppiness of the controls, which become light and easy to move but relatively ineffective because, with a reduced rate of airflow over them, there is less resistance to their movement.

When an aircraft stalls in level flight both wings, in theory, should lose lift and sink together. In practice, some aircraft will readily 'sink' in this fashion, others will not. Should one wing lose lift and drop before the other, use of the rudder may yaw the aircraft sufficiently to increase the airflow over the dropped wing and raise it again, but by the same token the airflow over the other wing will be reduced and the little remaining lift may well be lost. A dropped wing in an approaching stall cannot be corrected with the ailerons; the dropped wing has already exceeded the maximum effective angle of attack, so that depressing the aileron in an attempt to raise the wing will only increase its angle of attack (chord line to airflow, remember) and the aircraft will probably spin. The only cure for an approaching stall is more airspeed – either by pushing the nose down or giving more throttle, or both.

When an aircraft spins many complex factors can be involved, but in simple terms the spin will continue until a more or less equal degree of lift is restored to both wings. The rotation of the aircraft induces a degree of lift in the outer wing (at the expense of the inner) and so the unstable condition continues. Applying full opposite rudder, then pushing the stick steadily forward. will unstall the inner wing as the rotation ceases, and restore control.

Lift alone keeps an aeroplane in the air, so hold on to it.

Drag

Drag is the pilot's and the aircraft designer's enemy and is the sum of all the resistances offered by the aeroplane's shape as it passes through the air. The designer (among his many other problems) aims to produce a form that will reduce drag to a practical minimum, but he cannot avoid it entirely. Obviously a fully streamlined shape would be his ideal, but the pilot must have a reasonable, distortion-free area of vision and therefore the cockpit windscreen must project into the airflow; the engine needs air intakes for cooling and to feed the carburettor; radio aerials are required, and so on. As a result the designer must compromise between his ideal flying machine and one that is of practical use.

Drag can be divided into two components, known as **induced drag** and **profile drag**. The first is the inevitable price of lift, the second is the term for drag caused by all parts of the aircraft's structure, including the undercarriage and all other excrescences. Induced drag varies inversely as the square of the airspeed, while profile drag increases approximately as the square of the airspeed. This means in fact that induced drag lessens with greater airspeed, but profile drag increases. Induced drag is caused (induced) by the disparity in airflow pressures above and below the wings – a combination of aerofoil section and angle of attack. There is also some induced drag from the fuselage, tailplane, etc. In addition, there is a tendency for the air beneath the wing (higher pressure) to flow outwards and upwards round the wing tip to the lower pressure area above the

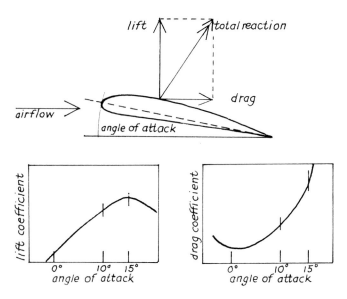

FIG 2.7

wing. This, with the backward movement caused by the aircraft's passage through the air, creates a twisting motion known as a wing tip vortex. It becomes visible as two white, smoke-like trails seen behind aircraft at certain altitudes when atmospheric conditions are suitable for this twisting air to condense into cloud.

Figure 2.7 shows the basic forces acting on the wing, and hypothetical lift and drag coefficients for a range of angles of attack. In practice the coefficients would change with speed and altitude, and with the designed aerofoil section. Note how the lift falls off rapidly as the critical angle is reached and how, likewise, the drag increases steeply.

Thrust

This is the force which compels the aircraft to move forward through the air. It is produced by the engine acting through the propeller. In normal level flight, thrust and drag must balance – be equal and opposite – for the airspeed to remain constant. Thrust is absent when an aircraft is gliding.

Weight

Weight acts vertically downwards through the aircraft's centre of gravity (C of G). For a light aeroplane it is almost constant for any given flight since the consumption of fuel at, say, 6 gallons or 20 kg per hour, for an aircraft with a total weight of perhaps 1 000 kg, is so nearly insignificant as to have little if any noticeable effect.

However, a four-seater aeroplane when fully-loaded with fuel, occupants and baggage, may well weigh 250–300 kg more than the same aircraft when the pilot is the only occupant. This will mean that for any given airspeed the aircraft, requiring more lift to balance the additional weight, will need to fly at a greater angle of attack or, in level flight, in a more nose-up attitude. This in turn means that the stalling angle (a constant) will be reached more readily and at a higher airspeed. Clearly, therefore, weight affects performance and some practical advice appears at the end of this chapter.

The four forces

The forces of lift, weight, thrust and drag are balanced in steady, level flight and appear as shown in Fig. 2.8.

For different flight conditions, however, they alter appreciably, for although weight continues to act vertically downwards, the other forces act in relation to the attitude or relative airflow. In a glide (Fig. 2.9) there is no thrust, and balance is achieved by the combined reaction of lift and drag (which has a vertical as well as a horizontal component) being equal and opposite to weight.

FIG 2.8

FIG 2.9

The balance of forces in a climb is shown in Fig. 2.10. From the diagram you will note that lift plus the vertical component of the thrust must balance the weight – which means, strangely, that as weight is a constant we have a smaller value for lift than in level flight.

FIG 2.10

Turning

When an aeroplane turns it is banked into the direction of the turn. This is in order to balance the centrifugal force which makes it tend to skid outwards – as would a car driven at speed round a sharp bend. The weight, as always, continues to act vertically downwards, but the lift

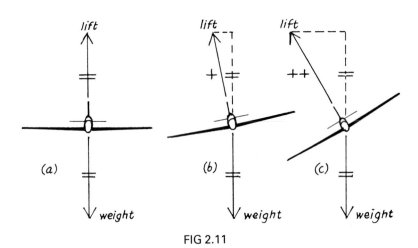

FIG 2.11

is inclined inwards and therefore only a portion of its total value is available to balance the weight. In Fig. 2.11 we can see how this creates a need for more and more lift as the bank increases with the steepening turn. If we go as far as 90°, or a vertically banked turn, the lift force is horizontal and, clearly, such an attitude can be maintained only momentarily, although in some aircraft types the fuselage shape is such that, when on its side, it can provide a small amount of lift.

To obtain the additional lift needed in a turn we can either increase our speed or increase our angle of attack. In practice we usually rely on the second of the choices, which means that for any given airspeed the wing is at a progressively larger angle of attack as the turn steepens. As a result, the wing is nearer to the stalling angle, which in turn indicates that the **stalling speed is higher in a turn than in level flight** (a fact remembered too late by many ex-pilots at low altitude). The increased angle of attack creates additional drag, so in order to maintain our entry airspeed for anything more than a shallow bank we must increase the power, using full throttle in a really steep turn.

The flying controls

It is not the purpose of this chapter to delve deeply into the practical side of flying the aircraft but having learnt a little theory you will wish to understand how this is applied in practice. A brief return to Fig. 2.1 will help here.

Basically, the handling of the aeroplane in the air is achieved by a **control column** or control wheel which, if pressed forward, causes the **elevators** (the hinged control surfaces attached at the rear edge of the fixed tailplane) to travel downward. The airflow beneath the depressed elevator surface exerts an upward pressure which raises the aircraft's tail and, as seen by the pilot, depresses the nose. If the column is moved backward, the reverse applies. Figure 2.12 shows these effects in diagrammatic form.

If the column or wheel is moved sideways it activates the **ailerons**, which are movable surfaces mounted at the wing trailing edges in the outer section of the wing. If the column is moved to the left, the left aileron is raised and the right aileron is lowered, and as each reacts to the pressure of the airflow the left wing goes down and the right wing comes up, giving left bank (column left, bank left). The reverse reactions apply, of course, if the column is moved to the right (column right, bank right).

Although in a modern aeroplane nearly all changes of the aircraft's attitude in the air are effected by the control column, our flying would be extremely uncomfortable and inefficient without a rudder. The **rudder** is the movable vertical surface behind the fixed fin (again, see Fig. 2.1), and is controlled by the pilot's feet moving the rudder pedals. Left foot forward moves the rudder to the left which, by swinging the tail to the

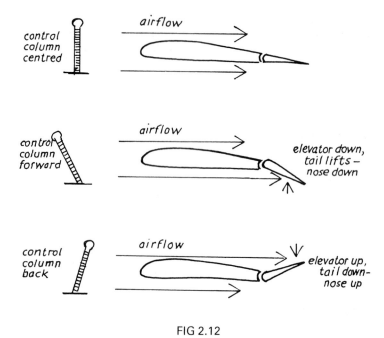

FIG 2.12

right in response to airflow pressure on the rudder, swings (or more technically correct, yaws) the nose to the left. See Fig. 2.13. This action produces
a degree of bank by increasing the speed, hence the lift, of the outer wing
as the aircraft yaws.

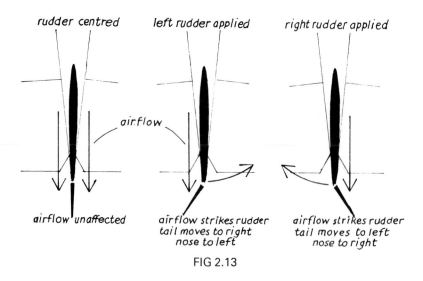

FIG 2.13

Turns are not made primarily with the rudder. To turn left we apply left bank (column to the left) and then a touch of left rudder to maintain what we call balanced flight, meaning that the aircraft neither slips inwards nor skids outwards as it turns. An experienced pilot can usually feel slip or skid, but even so an instrument is provided (turn and slip balance indicator) which gives a guide to the accuracy of the manoeuvre.

The aircraft axes
Reference to Fig. 2.14 clearly shows that an aeroplane has three axes about which it can be controlled:
(a) elevators give control in the pitching plane around the lateral axis
(b) ailerons give control in the rolling plane around the longitudinal axis

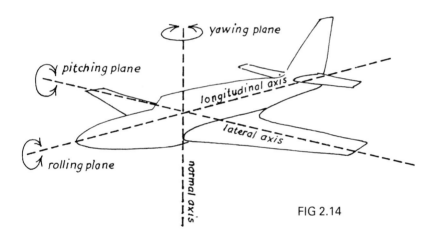

FIG 2.14

(c) the rudder controls the machine in the yawing plane around the normal (or vertical) axis.
The technical terms should be learnt but it is even more essential to understand the function and operation of the various controls, and Fig. 2.14 will help to make the terminology more understandable.

Stability
The fixed surfaces of the aeroplane's tail unit are there to provide stability. The tailplane is set at a smaller angle (the angle of incidence, which is fixed and must not be confused with the angle of attack which can be varied, as already explained) to the fuselage than is the case with the wings (or mainplanes), so when rough air disturbs the machine's fore-and-

aft attitude, the angle through which the tailplane moves is **proportiona-tely** greater than that of the wings. Let us look at an example – with the wings at 4° and the tailplane at 1°, a gust pitches the nose up through 2° so that temporarily the wings are at 6° and the tailplane at 3° angle of attack relative to the airflow. As a result the tailplane's lift increases substantially and so, by action in the pitching plane, lowers the nose to its original attitude.

Similarly the fin (see Fig. 2.1, again) provides directional stability. If the aeroplane is thrown off heading, say, to the left, the rear of the machine is yawed to the right, the airflow strikes the fin on that side and pressure causes the aircraft to return to its original attitude.

Lateral stability is usually provided in two ways. On low-winged mono-planes in particular, the wings are inclined upwards (the dihedral angle) as shown in Fig. 2.15(a). When the machine is banked by rough air the aircraft tends to slip in towards the lowered wing. The airflow, as shown in Fig. 2.15(b), meets this lower wing at a greater angle, and the higher

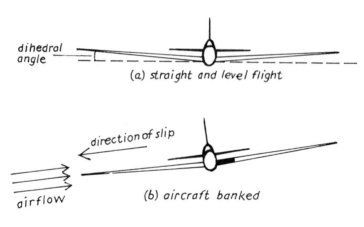

(a) *straight and level flight*

(b) *aircraft banked*

FIG 2.15

wing loses some of its lift (see shaded area) because it is partially shielded from the airflow by the fuselage. As a result the lowered wing is lifted, the raised wing lowered, and level flight is regained.

On an aeroplane with a high-set wing, the centre of gravity is well below the level of the wings and this provides a form of pendulum stability. In aircraft of this type a smaller dihedral angle is used.

Stability in itself is a major subject and one that can cause many problems for the aircraft designer. An unstable aeroplane (in any plane or in all three planes) would be very unpleasant to fly in any but undis-turbed air conditions, while a machine that is excessively stable resists all attempts to move it from its existing path, making the controls heavy and tiring and the machine insufficiently manoeuvrable.

Trimming

When the pilot wishes to change his aircraft's attitude – from level flight, for example, to a climb – he moves the controls to the appropriate position, but flying would be unnecessarily tiring if he were required to hold the column in the new attitude against the pressure of the airflow on the newly-positioned control surface. To avoid this he is provided with a trimmer, which he sets by means of a lever or a wheel in the cockpit. This setting moves a small tab at the trailing edge of the main control surface and, as shown in Fig. 2.16, pressure on the tab opposes that on the control surface itself. In the example shown a raised elevator would require a constant backward pressure on the control column if it was to be maintained in that position, but by lowering the tab and producing an upload the pilot can fly 'hands off' again.

elevator up
tab down

elevator down
tab up

airflow

FIG 2.16

All aeroplanes have elevator trimmers controllable by the pilot, but most light aircraft have to have their aileron trim pre-set on the ground, and normally only twin engined machines (which need substantial relief in directional loading when flying on one engine only) have rudder trimmers.

In some types of aircraft, spring or gear operated tabs are fitted to the elevators and are activated by movement of the control column. As the stick is pushed forward the elevators are depressed and the trimming tabs rise in proportion to the elevator movement.

Flaps

These may be the things you sometimes get into but right now flaps are surfaces fitted at the trailing edge of the wings, near the root or inboard section. They move downwards only and can be of a variety of types.

simple flap   split flap

FIG 2.17

Usually, they are either simple, in which case both surfaces of the trailing edge are lowered; or split, where only the lower surface of the trailing edge moves downward into the airflow. Both types are shown, partially lowered, in Fig. 2.17. Note that the chord line changes when flaps are lowered.

Flaps have several functions but one of their most significant roles is to enable landing approaches to be made more steeply than would otherwise be practicable. As already explained, a designer aims to produce an aeroplane that is subject to a minimum of drag. This in turn produces a flat gliding angle – which in many circumstances is beneficial – but it also means a flat approach when landing and difficulty in clearing obstacles close to the airfield. Lowered flaps, however, create additional drag and permit a steeper descent path, as shown in Fig. 2.18, without an increase in airspeed.

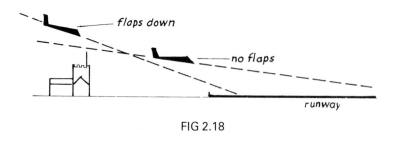

FIG 2.18

Although flaps primarily create drag, they produce some additional lift and when they are lowered through only a small angle this added value is the more marked. A small degree of flap, therefore, may be used for take-off and will enable the machine to 'unstick' at a lower airspeed and, therefore, in a shorter distance.

On most aircraft types, flaps can improve both the take-off run and the **angle** of climb, but because even slightly lowered flaps create some drag they reduce the aircraft's overall performance in that some of the available engine power is spent in overcoming that drag. As a broad guide, therefore, it may be wise to use flaps for the take-off and in the initial climb stage in order to avoid obstructions, but then to raise them in order to make a 'clean' aeroplane and to achieve the best climb **rate**.

Slats and slots

At the beginning of this chapter, when describing lift, we mentioned the airflow breakaway over the upper wing surface at the stall. On some aircraft types, however, this condition can be delayed by providing encouragement for the air to remain smooth through a larger angle change and, therefore, down to a lower airspeed. This is achieved by fitting thin slats, which are miniature aerofoil sections, just ahead of the wing leading edge.

FIG 2.19

They create a slot through which a layer of air will pass and be partially deflected into the pattern of the main aerofoil section. Slats can be fixed, automatic, or controllable from the cockpit. In the case of the automatic variety, the slats remain flush with the wing surface as long as the airflow over them remains streamlined. As the angle of attack is increased and the hitherto smooth airflow begins to break up in turbulent eddies, the slats move out into position, streamlining the airflow again.

It is important to lock automatic slats before aerobatics or deliberate spinning, and equally important to unlock them afterwards.

Aircraft performance

A pilot becomes accustomed to the performance capabilities of an aeroplane that he flies regularly, but if in doubt on any aspect he should consult the relevant publication or manufacturer's manual. However, performance can be affected, detrimentally, by several outside influences including extra weight, long and/or wet grass, an uphill slope for take-off (or downhill for landing), a slight tailwind, a hot sultry day, among many others. While any one of these may not put the operation at risk, several such conditions can combine and spell danger. It is worth remembering that professional pilots in operating their aeroplanes always consider their aircraft performance against the WAT limitations i.e. Weight (W), Altitude (A), Temperature (T) conditions.

Not only is the total, loaded weight extremely significant (some machines are overloaded when all seats, baggage space and fuel tanks are full) but load distribution can be critical (see Chapter 13). Heavy baggage in the wrong place can put the C of G outside the designed limits and render the aircraft unsafe.

All such matters can become a special hazard at a small private airstrip where the field surface, gradient and other pertinent factors may not be as familiar as they are at the home aerodrome.

3: Power plant and propeller

An aircraft's power plant is a collective term which includes the power unit (for our purpose the internal combustion engine), the propeller or airscrew, and the accessory installations such as generator, starter unit, fuel and lubrication systems, and so forth. Let's begin with the power unit, keeping the theory as simple as possible – you aren't required to be a mechanic or an engineer, but you should know the basic principles of your aircraft's power plant. After all, some pilot maintenance is now allowed for owners of light aircraft.

Power unit
This is the engine itself, made up of a number of cylinders, reciprocating pistons, intake and exhaust ports, together with their associated valves, rods, cams, etc, the crankshaft and case, spark plugs and so forth. The cylinders are below, above or about the crankcase and may be arranged in a variety of ways, such as horizontally opposed, V-shape, or round the crankcase to form a circle. In the latter instance the engine is known as a radial. Today, the majority of light aircraft engines are of four- or six-cylinders in an in-line or a horizontally opposed (flat) layout.

Power is generated inside the cylinders by rapid burning of a fuel-air mixture (petrol or diesel oil); the reciprocating pistons then transmit this power by connecting rods to the crankshaft which rotates within its crankcase. The propeller is driven, directly or through gearing, by the crankshaft and the power is thereby converted into forward motion of the aircraft.

As the piston moves up and down the cylinder chamber the power production cycle may be completed in two such travels (two-stroke), or in four travels (four-stroke). Two-stroke engines are favoured for mopeds and motor-cycles; here we will consider the operation of the four-stroke engine, which is the type normally found in light aircraft (and motor cars).

We have said that power is generated by burning a fuel-air mixture. During the process the mixture is drawn into the cylinder, compressed, ignited, rapid expansion follows, then the burnt gases (mostly carbon monoxide) are expelled ready for the next induction. All this is achieved in four travels of the piston in the following way.

1. Induction stroke. We begin with this stroke because it is the logical opening for the story but since we are dealing with a cycle it may commence at any point. At the beginning of the induction stroke the piston has just reached the topmost point of its movement and is beginning its travel downwards. Its complete downward journey is the induction stroke. The intake valve is open and the exhaust valve is closed. As the piston travels down the cylinder it creates an area of low pressure or suction above it, which draws in the fuel-air mixture through the intake port. The inlet valve will actually have opened slightly before the piston reached the top at the end of its previous stroke in the cycle. This is to allow more time for the mixture to enter the cylinder. (If the valve is opened too early, however, there is the danger of a backfire into the induction system.) For the same reason the inlet valve does not fully close until after the piston has reached the bottom of its travel and has begun its journey upwards. Throughout the induction period the mixture pours into the cylinder chamber. (See Fig. 3.1.)

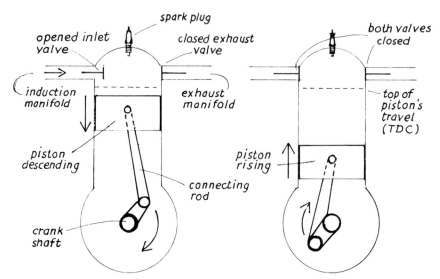

FIG 3.1 Induction stroke   FIG 3.2 Compression stroke

2. Compression stroke. Now the piston begins its way to the topmost position. Intake and exhaust valves will be closed and the fuel-air mixture is trapped above the piston head. As the piston travels up the cylinder it compresses the mixture, preparing it for efficient ignition. The compressed mixture (now at perhaps an eighth of its original volume at the start of the stroke) is ignited just before the piston reaches the top of its travel. Ignition is provided by a high-voltage spark jumping across the electrodes of the sparking plug fixed in the cylinder head. If the electrodes have become fouled by oil, carbon or lead deposits a short circuit may occur, causing the plug to misfire. If the spark plug has fired correctly the ignited fuel will have nearly burned out as the piston reaches the top of its stroke and will be trying to expand. (See Fig. 3.2.)

3. Power stroke. The two valves are still closed and the cylinder is airtight (piston rings around the piston prevent escape between the cylinder walls and the piston). The piston now begins its downward journey under the several ton load of pressure of the expanding gases which result from burning the mixture at some 1 700°C. This tremendous force acting on the piston is transmitted to the crankshaft by the connecting rod and converted to rotary motion. If the mixture has burned normally the piston will accept the pressure load smoothly, but if the burn-up was abnormal because of overheating of the cylinder, detonation will take place. When this occurs the piston is unable to convert its energy into torque energy satisfactorily and, consequently, heavy stresses are imposed on the whole cylinder-piston assembly. We will have more to say on detonation later, but the cylinder temperature may be too high because the aircraft is climbing steeply and there isn't enough cooling airflow, or because the fuel mixture is too lean (weak), or the engine is running at high rpm. (See Fig. 3.3)

4. Exhaust stroke. The exhaust valve is now open and the piston is travelling upward for the last time in the cycle. As the gases rush out through the exhaust port their acceleration creates suction above the piston; the intake valve opens just before the piston reaches the top of its travel and fresh induction flows in. This is the end of one complete four-stroke cycle and the beginning of the next. (See Fig. 3.4.)

FIG 3.3 Power stroke   FIG 3.4 Exhaust stroke

The fact that the intake valve opens early, before the end of the exhaust stroke, has a further advantage in that the fresh, relatively cool fuel-air mixture stays inside the cylinder that much longer, helping to cool it.

During the cycle, it was high temperature which produced the gas pressure to push the piston down. If all the heat generated was fully utilised by the power stroke we would have no cooling problem. As it is, some of the heat is absorbed by the cylinder wall, and something must be done to dissipate this heat quickly and efficiently before the cylinder and its working parts are damaged. In addition, detonation is always possible in an overheated condition.

In an air-cooled engine (water-cooled engines are now very rare) the cylinders are cooled by increasing their outer surface area in the form of cooling fins so that the heat dissipating area is also enlarged. The closer and deeper the fins the greater is the external surface available. The airflow is directed over the cylinders and the rest of the engine through an opening or openings in the engine cowling; inter-cylinder baffles may be used to force the airflow through the deepest fins.

Because of the possibility of detonation and the consequent danger to the engine it is very important to avoid excessive cylinder-head temperatures. A cylinder-head temperature gauge is part of the cockpit instrumentation of the less basic type of aircraft, the temperature information being relayed by means of a thermocouple attached to the known, hottest-running cylinder. Since the hottest cylinder has been chosen it may be assumed that the others are running at the same or lower temperatures.

A cylinder-head temperature gauge will show if the engine is sufficiently warmed-up before take-off. During flight, if the temperature rises above normal the cause must be determined and appropriate remedial action taken. The throttle may be used to control temperature. If the throttle is wide open there will be more combustion and therefore more heat, so if over-heating is due to excessive throttle, throttling back will cure it.

Wrong mixture may also be overheating the engine, in which case the situation is rectified by adjusting the mixture control. We will discuss this later (see page 38). Similarly, use of a carburettor pre-heating unit has a direct effect on engine heating and we discuss this aspect in the section which follows.

Carburettor

An internal combustion engine, as the name implies, is essentially a heat engine. It is a device in which fuel and air are mixed and burned in controlled conditions to produce heat energy, which is then converted to mechanical energy. The carburettor supplies this fuel-air mixture to the engine in the correct quantity and proportion ready for the cylinders to compress and ignite.

Of the various qualities required of the fuel, volatility and anti-knock properties predominate. Volatility is the readiness of the fuel to vaporise, and unless it does it will not burn. High volatility is called for particularly for starting the engine in cold conditions, but, on the other hand, extra-volatility always poses the danger of vapour locks in fuel pipes, and the chosen fuel is a compromise somewhere between the two.

The anti-knock property of the fuel is indicated by the octane number. Number 100 is iso-octane, a grade with very high anti-knock characteristics. The octane number is given as a percentage of iso-octane, 80, for example. Technically, the grading should run from 0 to 100 but, since the Second World War, fuels with better anti-knock value than 100 have been developed and consequently the grading system has been extended. In order to be able to recognise the octane grading visually, various colourings are used for the gradings. Light aircraft engines now operate on AVGAS 100LL (where the LL stands for Low Lead content). This grade is coloured BLUE which can be easily checked by looking through the filler orifice into the tank.

To get back to the carburettor, the present day version is quite an ingenious device. In this book we are not really concerned with its internal mechanism and there is a variety of makes and models on the market, each differing in some degree from the other. Some use a diaphragm instead of a float; some use a variable venturi instead of a fixed one – but the basic principles of carburettors remain the same. We will start with a look at a simplified carburettor, as shown in Fig. 3.5.

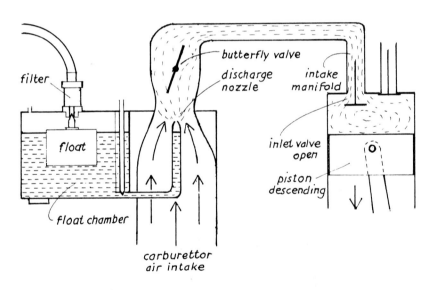

FIG 3.5

Initially, the fuel is pumped or is gravity fed into the carburettor's float chamber from the aircraft's fuel tank (or tanks). The float ensures that the fuel remains at the correct level in the jets. Fuel passes to the induction manifold via the carburettor main jet (in normal cruising flight, but there are other jets as well) into the venturi section of the carburettor. When the butterfly throttle valve is open, air can enter the carburettor from the carb intake scoop facing the airflow and mix with atomised fuel drawn from the jet. Thus the throttle in the cockpit controls the position of the butterfly valve which controls the air intake of the carburettor, and through that the fuel-air mixture and the power output.

When the piston in a cylinder is on the induction stroke its inlet valve is open and there is suction above the piston and in the induction manifold. Air rushes through the carburettor to fill this low-pressure area and, at the same time, fuel sprays from the jet nozzle near the throat of the venturi. The air and the fuel droplets mix together and acceleration takes place as they pass through the venturi (Bernoulli again, see page 11). This induces most of the fuel to vaporise and the process is essential if there is to be rapid and efficient burning of the mixture. The mixture travels along the induction system and is delivered to the appropriate cylinder for compression and ignition.

That is a simple carburettor. An operational version will be full of jets, nozzles, linkages and what have you, all intended to ensure accurate delivery of fuel and air over a range of conditions, speeds and altitudes as follows:

(a) correct mixture for all engine speeds
(b) correct mixture for slow-running
(c) correct mixture strength under variations of atmospheric pressure and temperature
(d) additional fuel for high-power setting
(e) additional fuel during accelerations – when the throttle is suddenly opened, air rushes in in larger quantity and will temporarily weaken the fuel-air mixture; an accelerator pump corrects the imbalance by supplying extra fuel, otherwise the engine would become erratic or hesitant – a condition known as flat spot.

Control of the carburettor is, first of all, by means of the control of the butterfly valve. For a given mixture ratio entering the carburettor, the rate of flow through to the cylinder is dependent on the position of the butterfly valve (which determines the power output of the engine). The more advanced the throttle setting, the freer is the passage through the carburettor and the greater the input of mixture to the cylinders. Easing back the throttle reduces the free flow and the input of the fuel-air mixture.

We mentioned the term mixture ratio in the above paragraph – the mixture of fuel and air – and this topic calls for special attention. We are dealing with air and liquid in action together, but although we can compress air and alter its weight for a given volume, a liquid does not generally compress. When the throttle is fully open, for instance, and there is a sufficient pressure existing in the induction system, the fuel-air mixture in pre-set proportions occupies the entire cylinder space available at the end of the induction stroke. That is, it occupies a given volume. The ultimate performance of the engine is based not on the volume, but

on the weight ratio of the mixture that fills the cylinder. In other words
it is the **weight of fuel and of air** admitted during each induction stroke,
not how many cubic feet or centimetres, that matters.

An engine will operate at full efficiency when approximately 15 kg of
air is mixed with 1 kg of fuel. This ratio of 15:1 is considered ideal. An
air and fuel mixture will still burn, however, when in a ratio of 7:1 –
7 kg of air mixed with 1 kg of fuel. A mixture of that ratio would be known
as **rich mixture**. It is rich because there is an increased weight of fuel
in a given weight of fuel-air mixture. At the other extreme, a mixture
can still be ignited when in a ratio of 20:1 – 20 kg of air to 1 kg of fuel.
Such a ratio would be a **weak or lean mixture**. Between the two extremes
we control the mixture to give the appropriate ratio for the flight, or
phase of flight. The adjustment is made with the cockpit mixture control
– a quadrant type of control with a lever which can be set at any point
from rich to weak. The setting chosen controls the quantity of fuel mixing
with air, it does not control the airflow. So let us see the effects of this
control assuming that our aircraft is fitted with a fixed-pitch propeller
and the throttle setting remains unchanged.

With the mixture control in the full rich position (usually forward but
not always so on some aircraft) the carburettor delivers a maximum quantity of fuel to mix with the airflow in the carburettor. Complete vaporisation will not occur and therefore there will only be a partial burning in
the cylinder. Maximum power is not produced and fuel is being wasted,
and there is a danger of carbon build-up in the cylinder head. If the exhaust
is visible, the indication of full rich will be seen as heavy black smoke
with a red flame at the tip.

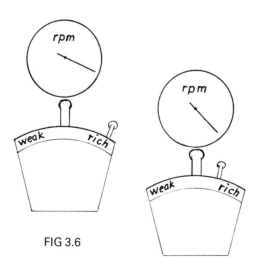

FIG 3.6

FIG 3.7

In normal flight as the lever is moved gradually from the full rich position you will notice a rise in rpm. This indicates that the fuel-air mixture is starting to burn more efficiently. As you continue to ease the lever and weaken the mixture the rpm will continue to rise for a time, then the rise will stop (see Figs 3.6 and 3.7). This position where the rpm stop rising, is called the **best rich** position. With this setting the mixture ratio is such that all oxygen particles are being burnt-out and the excess fuel is being utilised to cool the cylinder interior. The exhaust indication is blue flame. Rich mixture is normally used when operating at full power.

FIG 3.8

As you move the lever further the rpm remain unaffected for a while then the rpm begin to drop (Fig. 3.8). This new position, where the first drop in rpm is noticed, is called **lean best** position. Thus, between the two settings the rpm remain constant but the fuel consumption increases progressively from lean best towards rich best. The lean best position is ideal when cruising at medium power on a long run. This gives cruising power with fuel economy. However, watch-out for over-heating and signs of detonation, as lean mixtures can cause just that.

Any further weakening of the mixture causes loss of rpm, thus loss of power, overheating and, as an attendant consequence, detonation with a risk of engine failure. The manufacturer issues instructions on the use of the fuel-air mixture and these must be adhered to. This means that what your instructor says, goes. The notes here are only to be treated as a general guide. We may, however, add that if in doubt, prefer richer to weaker mixtures. We would also point out that the lever positions and rpm pointer indications in the above diagrams are for illustrative purposes only.

The second aspect of carburation is the effect on the fuel-air ratio due to variations in altitude. We emphasised earlier that it is the weight of the two constituents that matters. Suppose we are operating near sea level and the mixture control allows a ratio of 15 to 1 (15 kg of air to

1 kg of fuel). We then climb to 10 000 ft. Here, the atmospheric pressure is just about 75% of that at sea level, but the density of the fuel has not been significantly affected. Therefore at this level the induction charge contains 1 kg of fuel to about 11 kg (75% of 15) air. The intake by volume is still the same because the mixture still fills the combustion chamber; only the weight is less, due to reduced air density. In effect, although the mixture control lever hasn't been touched, the mixture has become too rich and it becomes necessary to lean-out the fuel (weaken the mixture) to preserve the original ratio. Thus, altitude changes call for mixture control adjustments. These changes may be effected by adjustment of the control lever but some carburettors incorporate an automatic device which maintains the set ratio.

As mentioned, the exhaust flames may give us an indication of the mixture we are using, but that's pretty rough and ready and often the pilot cannot see the exhaust. To take the guess work out of it a fuel-air ratio indicator is fitted in the cockpit of more sophisticated aircraft. If it is calibrated in some frightening figures like ·07 and ·08, etc. it still indicates the fuel ratio, but expresses it in decimals rather than in fractions. Fuel weight 1 kg, weight of air 13 kg, the fuel-air ratio is $\frac{1}{13}$. When you divide 1 by 13 you get the decimal value, which in this case is approximately ·077. This ratio is approximately your best power mixture.

Carburettor icing

Now let's take a look at the causes and dangers of carburettor icing.

Inside a carburettor all elements conducive to a temperature drop are present. The fuel-air mixture accelerates through the venturi, acceleration means a pressure drop, and in turn a temperature drop. There is a pressure drop in the induction manifold, which again means lower temperatures. As the mixture moves past the restriction caused by the butterfly valve it emerges once again in the full volume of the pipe, causing sudden expansion and again a temperature drop. The very fact that the fuel has to be vaporised causes a large temperature drop. Thus if there is any appreciable amount of moisture in the air it will condense out, freeze and ice will form. Commonly, icing begins near the throttle valve and works backwards through the carburettor passages, obstructing the mixture flow. Excessive icing near the throttle valve can jam the throttle.

Carburettor icing can be very hazardous and a close watch must be maintained when heavily moisture laden air or clouds are about, particularly when flying at low level. Use the carburettor heater whenever ice formation is suspected. A visible indication of icing comes from the tachometer (rev counter) which indicates a gradual falling of the rpm, but this symptom can easily be confused with engine trouble from a different source. The carburettor heater control in the cockpit usually has hot and cold positions, plus intermediate settings. When turned to 'hot', hot air is drawn from around the exhaust manifold, or the engine, and directed throughout the carburettor air intake scoop. The intake air temperature may be shown by a thermometer reading from the coldest point on the carburettor intake. Alternatively, there may be a mixture thermometer to indicate the temperature of the mixture as it leaves the carburettor outlet. The aim is to use the heater intelligently so that the temperature inside the carburettor does not fall below 0°C, but without raising the carburettor temperature unnecessarily. High carburettor temperatures mean reduced density – reduction in the weight of the charge to the detriment of the power output.

In flight, when ice has already formed, if the heater lever is shifted to hot, the effect becomes visible on the manifold pressure gauge, if fitted, which will show an increase in pressure passing through to the cylinder chamber. This is because the ice is being cleared and the fuel passages are becoming free of obstruction. On the other hand, if the heater control is set to hot when there is no ice present, a loss of pressure will soon show on the manifold pressure gauge. Note, too, that hot mixtures entering the combustion chamber can lead to detonation.

One answer to the problem of carburettor icing is the use of **direct injection** which dispenses with the carburettor and delivers a precise quantity of atomised fuel directly into each cylinder through an injection nozzle. The system has the further advantage of fuel economy as a result of the more accurate metering of the fuel-air mixture.

Supercharger

This is a centrifugal air pump placed between the carburettor and the intake manifold, its purpose being to pump a greater weight of air into the mixture and thus improve the overall engine performance. A supercharger is a rarity on light aircraft but may be installed to improve or boost the power performance at low levels, or to supplement the reduced air density at high levels. The fuel-air mixture from the carburettor, on entering the supercharger, first meets the impeller, a high-speed fan which gives the mixture a high velocity. The mixture then enters the diffuser unit where its speed is deliberately slowed down, so that the velocity energy is converted to pressure energy and the charge thus enters the combustion chamber at boosted pressure. The initial increase in velocity at the impeller stage produces a secondary advantage in that, due to the compression, vaporisation is more complete.

The pressure produced by the supercharger is called the manifold or boost pressure and an instrument known as the – wait for it – Manifold Pressure, or Boost Gauge, gives a reading of the pressure at the exit point of the supercharger.

To appreciate the usefulness of the supercharger consider the following points. The total weight of the charge that can be accepted by the cylinder depends first of all on the space available, which is a design feature. It depends, too, on the rpm – the faster you are turning the crankshaft the greater the induction appetite of the cylinders. Finally, it also depends on the pressure at which the fuel mixture enters the cylinder – which is where the supercharger comes in. The volume of the cylinder is a settled matter; we are not adjusting the rpm every other minute and can assume them to be constant; and flying in the same atmosphere, temperatures may also be considered constant. On the basis of these presumptions, the manifold pressure is an index of the power being produced. Manifold pressure is regulated by means of the throttle since the supercharger receives its charge from the carburettor.

In Fig. 3.9 we show the power unit, carburettor and supercharger, together with induction manifold and the tapping points for temperature and pressure measurements.

FIG 3.9

The manifold pressure gauge is calibrated in pressure absolute. This means that the atmospheric pressure is considered to be zero, and forms the base of the scale. Therefore, if you need to know the total manifold pressure all you have to do is to add 14·7 lb (atmospheric pressure at sea level) to the reading shown by the pressure gauge.

Manifold (or boost) pressures must be watched so that they do not become excessive. High manifold pressures can cause detonation. Insofar as the rpm and manifold pressures each have a bearing on power production, various combinations of rpm and boost pressure settings may give the same power output. With the object of preventing detonation only, a high rpm and low manifold combination is preferred but, obviously, high rpm mean high fuel consumption, so you've got to strike a balance.

Engine heating

We have mentioned the matter of overheating several times in this chapter. The topic is an important one, so let us regroup the basic elements conducive to overheating in a short summary.

1. Fuel-air ratio. Lean-out the mixture, by all means, in accordance with the operating instructions to effect economy when you are cruising at the specified percentage of rated rpm. Full rich on take off and when operating at high power output are the usual settings. Rich mixture, when operating at high manifold pressures, leaned-out sufficiently to give smooth engine running is the technique to avoid overheating.

2. Carburettor temperatures. High air-intake temperatures cause loss of efficiency plus overheating of the cylinder head. Use the carburettor heat sparingly.

3. Manifold pressures. High manifold pressures produce detonation, use mixture on the rich side to assist cooling.

4. Cylinder-head temperatures. These must not exceed the specified limits; watch particularly when the temperature of the incoming charge is relatively high.

5. Fuel characteristics. This is one we haven't mentioned before but it is most important. The fuel used must be of correct octane rating. Present day high-performance engines have been made possible by, among other things, the development of high-grade fuels able to withstand high pressures without detonating. The octane number is the fuel's anti-knock value. Use of higher octaine fuel permits the use of higher manifold pressures inside the cylinder but it can still detonate if the other controls are incorrectly set, or when operating under severe conditions.

Detonation

When the spark jumps across the gap between the electrodes of the spark plug it ignites the charge in its immediate vicinity. Ignition (or burning) then progresses steadily towards the centre of the cylinder where the pressures start to build up. At this time the piston is at top of its travel or just past it on its way down. The pressures increase very rapidly but the rate of build-up is quite steady, consequently the push exerted on the piston is smooth, increasing progressively.

When detonation occurs, the initial flame instead of burning smoothly and travelling to the centre of the cylinder, burns up almost instantaneously. The resulting pressures are abnormal and rise to a peak much faster than with normal ignition. Since neither the cylinder head nor the piston assembly is designed to absorb such loads the most likely consequence of frequent detonation is unit failure.

How do we detect the presence of detonation? It cannot be heard but, visually, black smoke with burning carbon particles floating away from the exhaust (if visible to the pilot) indicates detonation. On the instruments (when fitted), a high cylinder temperature is the surest indication, and unless there is another known explanation assume that detonation is taking place and throttle back without delay.

Sometimes detonation is confused with pre-ignition. **Pre-ignition** occurs when the charge in the combustion chamber ignites before the spark plug is activated, and may occur because of the overheated electrodes, carbon deposits, valves, etc. This again indicates excessive cylinder head temperature and a high-temperature air intake. Keep them within the specified limits. Pre-ignition occurs before the spark plug has fired; detonation occurs after the spark plug has fired. Pre-ignition can set off detonation; detonation can set off pre-ignition. Each is a danger to the health of the engine.

Fuel systems

Gravity-feed fuel systems are still found on many smaller aircraft because of their simplicity and reliability. The only real limitation to their installation is the design of the aircraft. In order to produce sufficient pressure in the line to send fuel from tank to carburettor the tank must be considerably higher than the carburettor. Thus the pressure in the lines depends on the vertical head of the tank. Figure 3.10 represents an elementary gravity feed system. The tank is usually made of aluminium alloy. All tanks are vented to the atmosphere to prevent build up of differential pressure and have a water drain at the lowest part. There are also water drains at the lowest points in the fuel system. Quality control of aviation fuel ensures that the fuel pumped into the aircraft tank(s) will contain a negligible amount of water. However, all aviation fuels absorb moisture from the air and whenever the fuel temperature is reduced some water is condensed out and, being relatively more dense than the fuel, sinks slowly to the bottom of the tank. Also in partly full tanks, changes in ambient temperatures can cause water to condense out (like dew) on the inside walls of the tank to contaminate the fuel. Overnight or for periods

FIG 3.10

of a few days, this latter problem can be minimised by keeping the fuel tanks full, especially if rapid temperature falls are forecast. Part of the aircraft's external checks involves the fuel drains – usually of the press up and twist type. When operated, only pure fuel should come from the drain. If water is suspected, the only satisfactory check is to collect the liquid coming from the drain into a clear (glass or perspex) container. If water is present it will settle in the bottom of the container with the lighter weight fuel above it. In these circumstances, the tank or fuel line must continue to be drained until it is certain that no more water remains. Baffles may be introduced internally to tanks to prevent interaction due to surging. An on/off cock controls the supply of the fuel at the start of the line. The purpose of the strainer, sometimes called a gascolator, is to prevent dirt or other foreign matter from entering the carburettor, and the carburettor itself usually has another small strainer to screen out any additional dirt. Leaving the main strainer, one line goes to the carburettor while the other goes to the engine direct via the priming mechanism.

Primer. A hand priming mechanism consists of a plunger type piston pump. When the plunger is pulled out (do it slowly) fuel is drawn into the pump. A slow pull ensures that the charge fills up the pump. When you push in the plunger, fuel is squeezed out into the cylinder – this operation is done smartly to help atomise the mixture. The technique is to give a few strokes of primer just before the starter is engaged, opening the throttle sufficiently to draw in the right amount of air to mix with the fuel. If the amount of air is too little the mixture is rich; similarly, too much air gives weak mixture. Both these mixtures burn too slowly and, as a result, when the intake valve opens on the exhaust stroke the mixture is still burning. This will ignite the incoming mixture which means that it will burn back into the induction system. This is backfiring, and is the reason why priming fuel is conducted in a line independent of the carburettor. Otherwise, with the carburettor lines full of fuel if the engine backfired a major fire hazard would exist.

Many aircraft cannot employ gravity-feed systems because of the design factors and/or the length of fuel passages involved. The latter, if nothing else, calls for much higher pressures in the lines. Such systems are fitted with an engine-driven fuel pump to produce the requisite pressure and to ensure positive delivery to the carburettor. Figure 3.11 shows some of the basic components. The system illustrated is a two tank system, a main tank and an auxiliary reserve tank. A reserve tank need not be installed as a separate unit; reserve facility can be provided by a standpipe in the main tank. Notice that it is no longer necessary to place the main tank above the level of the carburettor.

It is normal practice to incorporate a booster pump in conjunction with the tank. The pump may be inserted externally or may be submerged in the tank. A submerged booster pump is shown in the diagram. Its purpose is to provide positive pressure feed to the engine-driven pump – in other words, an intermediary between tank and fuel pump (Fig. 3.11).

FIG 3.11

A selector valve between the two tanks provides a choice of supply – the control lever is in the cockpit. (In larger multi-engined aircraft with a number of tanks the process of selecting tanks can be accomplished automatically, thus relieving the pilot of the need to keep a close watch over a fuel gauge when a tank is nearly empty.) Where the control is manual – a word of warning – never wait until the tank is completely dry. The changeover must be completed while there is still some fuel left. Also on some aircraft, auxiliary tank(s) may only be used in level flight or cruise, and fuel from the main tank(s) must be used for take-off, landing or going around.

The fuel pump supplies fuel to the carburettor at the correct pressure all the time that the engine is running. In fact it supplies more fuel than is required, in order to meet all circumstances. The excess fuel is removed by a relief valve at the pressure end of the pump and reintroduced in the line at the intake side.

The hand pump (Fig. 3.11) inserted between the main strainer and the fuel pump is meant to provide for emergencies. When operated, fuel travels through a bypass in the fuel pump, on to the carburettor. The hand pump also incorporates a relief valve to ensure that fuel at the correct pressure is supplied to the carburettor.

Multi-engine aircraft as well as twin-engine aircraft sometimes have one complete fuel system per engine. However, all these individual systems are interconnected so that should one system fail another system can be brought in to feed the starving engine. The cockpit control is called cross-feed control and it allows the pilot to use either tank for either engine.

Associated instrumentation. The following instruments associated with fuel systems are self explanatory:

1. Fuel pressure gauge (more sophisticated aircraft)
2. Low pressure warning light (on some light aircraft)
3. Fuel content gauge (essential)
4. Fuel flow meter gauge (larger aircraft only)

Obviously, your fuel is of vital importance. Know how much fuel you are consuming per hour at various rpm while cruising, and at full throttle. Know how much fuel you can lift (it may be less than full tanks if you are otherwise loaded). Be familiar with the location of all associated instruments in the cockpit together with the various fuel controls. Finally, your handbook has a diagram showing the aircraft's fuel system – study it, you will learn a lot.

Lubricating systems

The purpose of the lubricating system (also called oil system) is twofold: first, to provide a film of lubricant between moving parts to eliminate friction as far as possible (and thus heat and wear) and, second, to cool the engine interior.

We will begin by considering the properties of oil required to meet the problems of high temperature and bearing stresses present in an engine. First to be considered is the oil's **viscosity**, the degree of resistance to flow. If a liquid flows easily and rapidly it is said to have low viscosity; if it flows slowly it has high viscosity. If we use oil having high viscosity a more powerful pump will be needed in order to overcome the drag in the pipes, and starting the engine from cold may be difficult. If we use oil of low viscosity we have to remember that it thins out even further when it is warmed up. Viscosity is directly related to temperature. The danger is that the oil might thin sufficiently to pass up the cylinder walls above the piston and foul the spark plug. On the other hand, a thin oil has the advantage of flowing more easily and readily when starting in cold weather. From these considerations the oil we use must offer a compromise and provide an unbroken film under the highest temperatures. When a temperature regulating system is used, an intermediate viscosity oil does all this quite nicely.

Independent of the viscosity of the chosen oil another important factor is its flash point. It must have a high flash point, which means that it will not ignite when subjected to high temperatures. Another essential is that it must not change its chemical structure when heated or when in contact with acids and moisture in the engine. In other words it must be chemically stable.

In order to perform the tasks outlined at the beginning of this section, lubrication and cooling, the system works in two parts. The first part, incorporating a pressure pump, receives oil from the supply tank and circulates it under pressure to various parts of the engine requiring lubrication.

The delivery pressure is tapped at a convenient point and indicated in the cockpit on the oil pressure gauge. There are several parts in the engine, such as cylinder walls and pistons, where the oil is required in the form of a spray, and this is produced by the revolving crankshaft. The system incorporates a pressure relief valve in association with the pressure pump. If the pump produces a higher pressure than is necessary the relief valve regulates it, the surplus oil being returned to the supply tank or to the scavenger system.

The second task, of cooling the engine, is performed by the **scavenger system**. As the oil circulating round the engine absorbs heat it is drained down the engine into a receptacle called the scavenging sump at the lowest part of the crankcase. A pump, known as the scavenger, pumps out the oil as fast as it arrives and sends it back to the supply tank for re-use via a unit known as the oil temperature regulator (or simply, oil cooler).

The oil cooler unit consists of a section of core tubes through which the air flows, the core section being surrounded by a metal jacket (see Fig. 3.12). A thermostatically controlled valve directs the oil either round

FIG 3.12

the core or through the outer shell direct to the tank, depending on the temperature of the incoming oil. This by-pass allows a quick warm-up after starting. A thermometer placed between the supply tank and the engine gives temperature indications in the cockpit. To help control the temperature a shutter flap is installed on the exit side of the oil cooler. The operation of this flap from the cockpit regulates the airflow in the core of the oil cooler and thus the oil temperature.

In cold weather the oil will be congealed and give a difficult start. To overcome this difficulty many devices have been perfected. One which gives quite satisfactory results dilutes the oil with a small percentage of engine fuel, but it is unlikely to be found on the average light aircraft. The dilution control is employed for a short time just before switching off the engine when a cold start is anticipated. This action allows fuel from the pressure line to enter the oil system and to dilute the oil, so that, when the cold engine is started, the thin oil circulates rapidly and as the engine approaches its normal temperature the fuel element evaporates, leaving the oil in its normal state.

On the operational side, be careful not to fill the oil supply tank to the top – all liquids require some space for expansion when warmed up. When starting the engine, particularly on a cold day, high oil pressure will be indicated at first. This is because high viscosity oil is circulating but it is quite possible, in spite of the high pressure indicated, that the actual oil circulation is inadequate. To protect the engine against this possibility it is a good plan not to run it up to high rpm until it is warm and the pressure readings are meaningful.

Hydraulics

Hydraulics is not a subject in the PPL aircraft general examination syllabus but we give it here as useful background information for the aircraft type syllabus.

The hydraulic system is used in an aircraft mainly to operate such mechanisms as landing gear and flaps. There are several different systems in existence but all utilise the basic property of incompressibility of liquids. The basic components and the theory behind their use also remain the same in all systems. In this section, we shall build up an elementary system, so that when this is read in conjunction with your own aircraft notes you will have a better understanding of its hydraulic system.

The fluid used in the hydraulic system is oil. If you have a can of water full to the top you know that you cannot add another drop without it running over. This is because it will not compress. So, if you could apply a force on the top of the liquid and it did not compress, what would happen to the applied force? Well, the force would be transmitted nearly intact (frictional losses are negligible) to the bottom of the can. If a force of one pound per square inch force could be applied to the top, the same one pound per square inch force will be felt at the bottom.

So far so good, but the advantage of this property of liquids lies in the fact that, if the base of the can was wider than the top, the pressure on the bottom would still be one pound per square inch. In this way for a small pressure at the narrow end of the system a large pressure can be produced at the wider end.

In practice, a piston is fitted in the smaller cylinder and is used to exert pressure on the liquid. This is connected to a larger cylinder by

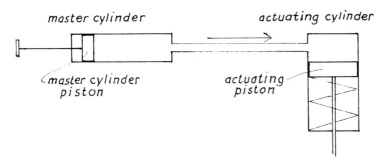

FIG 3.13

means of a pipe. There is a similar fitting piston in the larger cylinder which is activated under pressure of the liquid.

Before we work out an elementary hydraulic system it is worth remarking that, unlike fuel and lubricating systems, the hydraulic system remains in constant readiness but is only active when its service is called upon, e.g. selecting undercarriage down. Furthermore, the system must accommodate a two-way operation of the various mechanisms, e.g. the flaps may be selected down, then up again. We will now see how the system meets this requirement.

Let us again take two cylinders with their fitting pistons. The smaller cylinder on the left in Fig. 3.13 is called the master cylinder; the larger one on the right is the actuating cylinder. Let us assume for that moment that the piston in the actuating cylinder is kept in the up position by means of a spring. This then becomes one position for whatever gear is operated by this actuating pump. Now, apply force to the master cylinder

FIG 3.14

piston until it has pushed all the fluid from the cylinder. The fluid thus forced out will enter the actuating cylinder and exert pressure, the piston being forced down the cylinder as a result. Snag? Yes, although the pressure in the actuating cylinder is sufficient to move the piston, the distance that it will travel is limited by the total amount of fluid displaced from the master cylinder. Therefore the master piston will have to make several strokes to get the actuating piston to the bottom of its cylinder. But the master cylinder is now empty, so we must insert an oil reservoir in the system from which the master cylinder can refill after each stroke of the piston. This addition is shown in Fig. 3.14.

The next thing we have to do is to prevent the expelled fluid from rushing back to the master cylinder when the pressure from the master piston is removed, otherwise we will not be able to build up pressure in the actuating cylinder. So, we will insert a non-return valve between the master and actuating cylinders for this purpose, and for similar reasons, we will insert another non-return valve between the reservoir and the master cylinder so that when fluid is forced out by the piston it cannot return to the reservoir. As a result we have a system as shown in Fig. 3.15.

FIG 3.15

We now have a supply of fluid, available on demand, from the reservoir and by operating the piston in the master cylinder we can fill the actuating cylinder. The piston in this cylinder is now down, and the gear or mechanism connected to it is in the reverse position – if the flaps were down before, then they are up now. The oil in the system is held under pressure, by the non-return valves and the piston will remain down. When we wish to select the alternative position for the gear or mechanism, we will have to release the pressure so that the piston may be forced up by the return spring. But with the system shown in Fig. 3.15 the pressure cannot be released, so we must now introduce a return line to the reservoir and a selector valve to enable us to select either position. Lastly, since a spring cannot be expected to lift an undercarriage we will replace it with a second hydraulic line to operate the actuating piston in the other direction, as shown in Fig. 3.16.

FIG 3.16

Of course, for pumping we can use a power pump, retaining a hand pump for emergencies and ground checks. Such, then, are the major components of an elementary hydraulic system and the whole picture is as shown in the diagram.

Although in emergencies a hand pump may be used, with most systems there is a further source of pressure available in case the hand pump fails, supplied by a unit called the accumulator. It comprises two hemispherical sections joined together – one hemisphere contains compressed air, the other fluid, and the two are separated by means of a diaphragm. The accumulator's main purpose is to store hydraulic fluid under pressure and to be available in emergency.

All hydraulic fluids are inflammable. If there is a burst pipe and fluid leaks into the cabin, windows must be opened for the fumes to disappear (in an unpressurised aircraft). In any case, adequate fire precautions must be taken promptly.

Ignition system

The purpose of the ignition system is to provide an electric spark to the appropriate cylinder at the correct moment to ignite the fuel-air mixture. The system includes an electrical source, a breaker assembly, a condenser, a distributor unit and an ignition switch.

Whenever there is relative motion between magnetic flux and a conductor, electric voltage is generated. This relative motion can be arranged in any of three ways: the magnetic flux is stationary and the conductor moves; the conductor remains stationary and the magnetic flux moves; or the conductor is stationary the flux varies. Single or dual magnetos provide the source of electricity in an aircraft ignition system. A magneto itself may utilise a two-pole, four-pole or eight-pole magnet system depending on the size of the work to be done. Around the magnet there is a soft iron core (or ring) wound with coils of heavy wire. This winding is known as the primary coil. Around the primary coil there is another winding of fine wire, called the secondary coil. The magnet is rotated by means of an accessory shaft from the engine. Associated with the magneto unit is an automatic switching device called the breaker assembly. Its function is to make and break the primary coil circuit.

As the magnet rotates the breaker circuit is closed, the primary circuit is complete and a mild current flows through the primary coil. This current produces magnetic flux which cuts the windings of the secondary coil. A little later the breaker assembly opens the primary circuit, the current is interrupted and there is a collapse of the flux. This collapsing flux cuts the secondary winding at extremely high speed and induces a very high voltage in the secondary coil. The magnitude of this induced voltage depends on the number of windings in the secondary coil as against the primary coil (the secondary to primary ratio). The voltage is around 15 000 to 20 000 volts.

The breaker assembly consists of two contact arms, one rigid and the other flexible. When the primary circuit is closed, the contact points on the two arms are together. An instant later a cam on the rotating accessory shaft lifts the flexible contact arm and breaks the circuit. These two breaker points are usually made of high grade platinum and it is important that they are smooth and clean for a perfect contact. The timing of the opening and closing of the breaker points must be such that the circuit will be broken (and a high voltage induced) at the precise moment when the spark is required for the cylinder.

The purpose of the condenser is to absorb the surge of the current when the primary circuit is interrupted and thus assist in an instantaneous collapse of the flux. Furthermore, it is connected in parallel across the breaker assembly and prevents arcing or burning of the breaker points.

The high voltage produced in the secondary coil is fed to the spark plug in the designated cylinder via a distributor unit. This unit consists of a plate over which a pointer, called the distributor finger, rotates at half the crankshaft speed. The plate has a number of blocks or contact points and when the distributor finger carrying the high voltage from the induction coil passes over one of the blocks the circuit to that particular cylinder is completed and the voltage delivered to the spark plug. The order in which the cylinders are fired depends on the design of the engine. The firing order of a four cylinder in-line engine is $1 - 3 - 4 - 2$.

The ignition switch, apart from opening or closing the ignition circuit, provides a means of testing the correct functioning of the magnetos when a dual magneto system is installed. Each of the two ignition switches is switched off in turn and the fall in the rmp noted – the fall should be very small. Any heavy mag drop (as it is called) suggests unserviceability of the unit.

Dual magnetos give an added safety margin in that if one system fails the other one will keep you going until you can land at the nearest suitable point. They also contribute to burning the mixture more completely in the cylinder.

Electrical services

The electrical service to various instruments and equipment is provided by generators, inverters (or alternators) and batteries.

Generators meet the DC (direct current) requirements of the system and help keep the battery fully charged at all times. All generators have a rated power output. To prevent too much power overloading the equipment, voltage and current regulators are inserted in the system. Furthermore, in order that at lower power output the battery charge does not drain into the generator, a cut-out relay is incorporated between the two. This relay operates at a predetermined power output of the generator. Its functioning is checked by reducing the rpm to a given value and noting if the generating failure light comes on as it should.

The AC (alternating current) requirement for radio, radar and other equipment is met by an inverter or an alternator. As the name suggests, AC changes its direction half way through each cycle. Certain equipment requires one-, two- or three-phase AC. In a single-phase, a single current flows in the circuit. In two-phase AC, two single-phase currents pass through any given point in the circuit, one current 90° ahead of the other. In a three-phase AC, three currents pass through the same point in the circuit at 120° from each other.

The battery in itself provides a short term source of DC reserve in the event of generator failure occurring. It may also be used to start the engines when an external battery is not available. In this case it would be useful to start the engine with a generator first so that further drain on the battery is reduced when starting the second engine.

Should a generator fail, all unnecessary electrical services should be switched off to conserve the life of the aircraft battery. To protect the electrical system against risk of fire or damage to equipment due to overloading, each electrical circuit is normally provided with a fuse or a circuit breaker – usually in the form of a cartridge fuse or a reset thermal trip circuit breaker. If a fuse blows or a circuit breaker, trips and you cannot see any evidence of damage and there is no smoke or strange smell, still allow at least two to three minutes to let the circuit cool down before you reset the circuit breaker or replace the fuse. If it blows again, switch off the services on that particular circuit.

For further information on AC phases the student is referred to Volume 1, Chapter 1 of 'Ground Studies for Pilots'.

Propellers

The aircraft engine delivers power (bhp) to the propeller shaft, the propeller converts the power into thrust and drives the aircraft through the air. In earlier days when aircraft speeds and ranges were relatively small, fixed-pitch propellers did the job quite nicely. This type of propeller (of wood or alloy) is still retained on smaller aircraft, mainly because of the low cost and lightness.

As the propeller blades turn and move through the air, they produce the same type of reaction as any other aerofoil surface of the aircraft. That is why, like the wings, the angle of attack that the blades make with the airflow is vitally important when assessing a propeller's efficiency. This angle, or pitch is normally around two degrees. Because the tip of the blade travels faster than the section near the hub as the propeller travels forward, a flat-shaped blade would present a varying angle of attack right through its length. Thus the 'twist' in the blade produces a near constant angle of attack all the way through. The angle near the hub is highest, that near the tip lowest.

With a fixed-pitch (or a fixed-blade angle) propeller no adjustment of the blade angle is possible. It is designed to turn with maximum efficiency at a predetermined relative and forward speed in level flight. In such conditions the engine is able to run at its rated value, but it produces less than its rated bhp during take-off and in a climb. However, fine or coarse pitch blades may be fitted for specific purposes, such as glider towing, or long-range touring.

As aircraft grew larger, faster and more powerful, increased propeller efficiency became necessary. If the propeller blades could be adjusted in the air to suit a particular circumstance it would be equivalent to giving gears to a racing car. Development on these lines went through various stages, beginning with a ground adjustable propeller. The blade angle was pre-set to suit the anticipated operating conditions. Then came the two-position controllable propeller and finally variable-pitch and the constant speed types.

Constant-speed propellers may be likened in some ways to automatic gears in motor cars. You first set the pitch control and the propeller adjusts the pitch of its blades in response to the throttle setting. During take-off the blades will be set to fine pitch to permit the high rpm necessary. As you level out and reduce your throttle setting and rpm requirements, the blades will set to coarser pitch, thus increasing the air resistance and relative thrust of the propeller and decreasing the rpm. Afterwards, any change in the altitude, attitude or throttle setting will automatically adjust the blades to an appropriate angle to hold the rpm. The extent of the blade travel from finest to coarsest pitch is limited by a stop. At the lower limit the fine angle gives maximum rpm; at the coarse limit the blade angle is such as to prevent over-speeding in a steep dive.

Operationally, with a fixed-pitch propeller the rpm are controlled by the throttle; with a variable-pitch propeller the rpm are controlled by the propeller. Thus, within the constant-speed range of the propeller, the opening of the throttle has no effect on the rpm.

The principal advantage of a constant-speed propeller over a fixed-pitch propeller is that it permits the engine to develop its full rated power in all flight conditions. The propeller always operates at the most efficient angle and thus, for example, makes it possible to shorten the take-off run of a heavy aircraft.

As already mentioned under Engine Heating, when operating in the high power range the use of low rpm with high manifold pressure is not advised because of the risk of detonation. Also, as general practice, when increasing to high power the rpm should be increased first followed by the manifold pressure and when decreasing power, the manifold pressure should be reduced first.

When it became possible to adjust the blade angle in flight, feathering became possible. Feathering means that the blades are shifted beyond the coarsest angle point and become aligned with the airflow. In this position they do not windmill, and offer the least possible drag. A propeller is feathered in the event of an engine emergency such as failure or a fire. Finally, if the angle of the blades is adjusted still further, so that the reverse side of the blade now faces the airflow (reverse pitch), very effective braking action results.

On the ground, when the engine power checks are carried out, a variable pitch propeller is 'exercised' through its whole range at least once to check that the constant speed unit is functioning properly and the oil in it is circulating satisfactorily. The feathering part of the CSU range is usually protected by a detent or similar in the propeller control slot and there are normally specific instructions on its operation in the aircraft manual.

4: Maps and charts

It is written that an area map must be carried in flight. In this chapter, our purpose is to examine lightly one or two types in general use. And lightly is the word, for the actual transference of a curved surface onto a plane one is a complex exercise, introducing specialised mathematics – so, let's just paddle around the shallow end.

Maps illustrate certain features of the Earth's surface on sheets of paper, while charts are but outlines of special conditions such as magnetic influences, population densities or whatever. Each calls for some reference to the place and area shown; this is done by lines of latitude and longitude.

Latitude
The circle round the globe which is equidistant from either Pole is the Equator, labelled 0°, nought degrees, of latitude. To the North and South of the Equator, imaginary circles are drawn at parallel intervals until the Pole is reached at 90°. The Pole is a point, so it follows that the concentric circles of latitude are getting smaller and smaller until the Pole is reached.

Latitude is classified in degrees, minutes and seconds, labelled North or South of the Equator; it is in fact an angle measured between the plane of the Equator at the centre of the Earth and the point in question. A degree consists of 60 minutes of arc, a minute of 60 seconds, but seconds are not in frequent practical use.

Remember now and forever that one minute of latitude is one nautical mile, or 6 080 feet (1′ lat = 1 nm).

The only parallel of latitude that cuts the Earth into two halves is the Equator. Any line that does this is a Great Circle, and it is a fact that on the surface of the globe the shortest distance between any two points is the arc of the Great Circle through them. All other parallels of latitude do not bisect the Earth, and are small circles.

Longitude
The division here is rather different. A line is drawn from the North Pole to the South Pole passing through Greenwich, labelled 0°. Similar lines are drawn in through every spot on the Equator and are known as meridians. Eventually, a meridian will be reached which is a continuation of the Greenwich 0° meridian over the Poles: this is the ante-meridian of Greenwich, labelled 180°. All other meridians are measured in degrees, minutes and seconds, labelled East or West of Greenwich, until a second short of the 180° meridian.

You will have spotted that a meridian and its ante-meridian bisect the globe, and form a Great Circle. A meridian is thus a semi-Great Circle.

But a degree of longitude is useless as a measurement of distance, since it gets smaller and smaller as either Pole is approached. Only on the Equator itself can a degree of longitude be considered as 60 nm, a minute of longitude as 1 nm, for this is like a meridian with its ante-meridian, a Great Circle.

The expression of position of a point on the Earth's surface is no doubt well known to you. London Airport is 5128N 0027W, for example; and the symbols for degrees (°), minutes ('), and seconds if any ("), are generally omitted. It is North of the Equator and West of Greenwich, and figures are given complete, noughts included. Honiara in the Solomon Islands is 0926S 16003E, meaning its Latitude is 9 degrees 26 minutes South of the Equator, its longitude 160 degrees 3 minutes East of the Greenwich meridian.

The picture of intersecting parallels of latitude and meridians of longitude is called the graticule.

Scale

A map or chart is quite useless without a scale. A section of the Earth's surface has been transferred to a sheet of paper with a considerable reduction in size, and for a flight between two places the pilot needs a measurement on his map which will tell him at once the actual distance on the Earth. This is usually done by measuring the distance in minutes up the latitude divisions on a nearby meridian, which will give the distance in nautical miles. The type of trip and the equipment in the airplane determines the maps to use. A flight of 50 nm to land on a farmer's airstrip means a large scale map, but a flight of some hundreds of miles between airports in a fast aircraft full of radio-navigation equipment does not.

There are several ways of stating scale on a map. One is a straightforward statement in words, such as 1 inch to the mile; this is rather unpopular in aviation circles, perhaps because it smacks of the Army or motorists, but more likely because it might refer to a statute mile which is a thing to be utterly disregarded. Another way is the graduated scale line, showing the map distance of one to about a hundred nautical miles, nicely divided up, and placed in one of the margins. The third and general way is the representative fraction, the ratio of one unit on the map to the number of same units it represents on the Earth's surface; it is immaterial what the units are. So 1:500 000 means that 1 inch on the map represents 500 000 inches on the Earth; or 1 centimetre represents 500 000 centimetres on the Earth; one of whatever you like represents 500 000 of the same, but no mixing of units, of course. Similarly, 1:250 000 means say 1 inch on the map represents 250 000 inches on the Earth: this scale is loosely referred to as the ¼ in to the mile – very loosely, so it's seldom heard in the flying clubs.

The graduated scale line and the representative fraction are in constant use by private pilots. It is worth mentioning that the larger the denominator the smaller the scale, as more of the Earth's surface will have been contracted into the one unit – and, in consequence, much information and detail must be omitted. However, precise detail for map reading in a fastish aircraft can be unnecessary and the larger sheets are difficult to handle in a confined and awkward cockpit space. While on this point there is a distinct art in folding a map for use on a cross-country flight. Be guided by your flying instructor on how to map-fold most efficiently.

Projection

The trappy business of getting a portion of the sphere onto a flat surface has given much mental exercise for generations. By taking a model globe, putting a light at the centre (or anywhere inside, actually), a reflection of the graticule can be cast on to a sheet of paper held flat at a chosen point on the globe, wrapped round it as a cylinder, or as a cone. Thus we get the term 'projection' for a map, and the types are very many indeed. Nowadays, they are nearly all resolved by mathematics to suit a particular purpose. We are concerned with two particular projections, suited for flight requirements – and these, fortunately, only with regard to their properties and practical use.

Lambert's Conformal Conic Projection 1:500 000

This is often called Lambert's Orthomorphic Conic, and it means the same thing, but we'll come to that shortly, as the whole thing has an academic flavour – in our opinion, unjustifiably so.

The map was developed by Johannes Lambert a few hundred years ago from the simple conic projection, hence its name, and it has proved just the job for airmen. Its use is increasing rather than dropping out of favour. For your interest only, instead of the cone being slapped on the model globe to fit round some chosen parallel of latitude, it is presumed to slice through the crust intersecting at two parallels (Fig. 4.1). A packet of mathematical adjustments is then made to the resultant shadow of the graticule to produce the Lambert's Conformal. The 'conformal' bit in the title means that angles measured on the chart conform to angles measured on the ground. The scale at any point is the same in all directions. For all practical pilot-navigation purposes scale may be considered 1:500 000 over the whole chart although this is only strictly true along the two standard parallels of latitude.

A moment's thought will convince you of the irregular distortion which results from projecting part of the sphere onto a cone which is then unrolled; this distortion is corrected all over the sheet, and the map is conformal or orthomorphic. When you buy your chart, pay the extra few pence and get one with a laminated finish. They have a far longer life than the simple paper versions and you can easily wipe off any stains from any spilt liquid you may have used to sustain your pre-flight planning sessions.

The scale is given at the top of the chart as a representative fraction, and also in a margin as a graduated scale line for each of nautical miles,

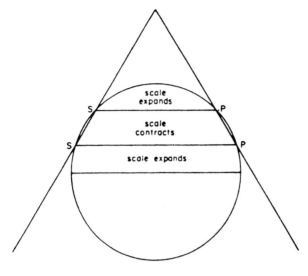

FIG 4.1

statute miles, and kilometres – a good idea, this, for the see-saw of nautical miles and kilometres at home and abroad can be confusing.

If you look at one of these maps – for example, Southern England and Wales – you will notice a comprehensive legend of chart symbols. These are also detailed in the Appendix to the 'master' green Aeronautical Information Circular which gives particulars of all ICAO charts available in the UK. You are required to have a working knowledge of the more general ones, especially the various types of aerodromes; areas prohibited, dangerous or restricted; obstructions; the various zone boundary markings. Aerodromes where Customs facilities are available have a pecked line round the name; a figure nearby indicates the height of the field above mean sea level (amsl). Where space permits, the runway layout is depicted on the aerodrome symbol. If the aerodrome is active and has a landing strip of 1 829 m or more, a dot is placed in the centre of the symbol. So there's an immediate introduction to mixed units – height in feet, runway length in metres; there is a conversion table in the map margin, but the computer is used for this sort of thing, and we have a chapter on its use.

Check a few samples of symbols, at the same time getting a little practice in finding a place by its lat and long; the Douglas protractor and a pair of dividers will soon lead you to the simplest and most accurate method of finding or plotting an exact position; in Figs. 4.2, 4.3, 4.4 we have reproduced the areas from the SE corner, ISLE OF WIGHT region and the NW corner of the chart. On your current chart find:

LYDD	(5058N 0057E)
VALLEY	(5315N 0432W)
SHOREHAM	(5050N 0017W)

FIG 4.3

ELEVATIONS IN FEET

Which are Customs aerodromes? what are their elevations amsl? which are military? civil? both? which have runways over 1 829 m long? Check from the conversion table that 1 829 m is just about 6 000 ft. Did you go East of the 0000 meridian to find LYDD? and West of the 0400W meridian to find VALLEY?

The symbols for obstructions are another item to watch. The height amsl is given on the map in italic figures, while the height above ground (agl) is given in brackets, always in feet, but disregarded if below 300 ft agl. Learn this one well, for in flight a pilot is generally concerned with heights amsl, but on approach and take-off, height above gound is the more important. Look at the DOVER area where M. Bleriot was aiming for a few examples.

Relief on this chart is by layer tinting, the deeper the colour the higher the ground. The legend is in the margin, and it should be said now that colours for layer tints in the various topographical (that is, the mapping of ground features) maps you'll encounter are by no means standardised, so if you pick up a new map in some remote foreign field, check the legend at once. And watch the units of elevation; here they are in feet, spot heights are in feet, but the legend does convert to metres for you. The fact of elevations being in feet is drawn to your attention no less then six times in the margins, so the mappers are trying to help. The highest danger spots in an area are given in large characters on a white background. Look at the SNOWDONIA area in Fig. 4.4 in which the greatest elevation $\boxed{3\,559}$ is identified. This is also clearly given at the top of the legend for RELIEF PORTRAYAL. The layer tint method of showing elevation is easily more popular than that system so bashed out in school geography – contours, lines joining all places of equal height, each line labelled; thus, tight close contours would indicate a steep slope. It is used though on the map we are looking at, but generally the cartographers are pretty hard put to it to decide what to leave out in flying matters.

There is another set of artificial lines which you must know of, dashed, running down and across the map, marked 5°00W, 6°00W, 7°00W, with a date underneath. Trace one or two of these from the lowest latitude. These are isogonals, lines joining all places of equal magnetic variation; this topic is dealt with in a separate chapter, and it is imperative that you are fully conversant with it, since you will be steering direction with reference to the Magnetic North Pole in order to find your way over the Earth mapped with reference to the True North Pole. That's whetted your appetite, so we will now look at the other map.

The UK 1:250 000 topographical chart

The projection is called the Transverse Mercator, and for practice try using your local flying area sheet; this title is kept mysteriously quiet in the laid-down syllabus, as it could possibly make prospective pilots buy a power boat instead but it's in the green AIC. For this projection, a cylinder was placed round the model globe, touching the globe at a chosen meridian and its ante-meridian; the resultant graticule thrown on the cylinder by the central light source was a very peculiar thing indeed, but as usual the idea formed the basis of a mathematical foray to produce a chart which preserved some of the aeronautically worthwhile properties.

Note that this map is a larger scale, and only covers a little more than one degree of latitude; it would be useful on local flying only, and several sheets would be required for anything more than the shortest cross country. It has more detail – much more is made of roads, railways, tunnels, befitting the larger scale. All symbols are as usual (by more or less international agreement) and we check that elevations are in feet, though spot heights are given in strong figures, black, straight on the chart.

Plotting positions can be done as easily as before, since minutes of lat and long are marked off on parallels and meridians every half-degree. You should plot a few odd positions to get familiar with the chart's layout.

Properties of both charts

You may take it that, for all practical purposes, these charts have a constant scale and that a straight line is a Great Circle. These are immensely important properties in flying, for a straight line on the chart coincides with a line drawn between the two points on the globe, passing over the same landmarks on the map as on the earth; and with constant scale, distances on the chart are as for the globe, and the same goes for angles measured at a meridian. The projection of a curved surface on to a plane sheet can, in these two cases, be considered a howling success from the pilot's point of view.

Measuring tracks and distances

Let's get on with the real job – using the maps to prepare for a cross country flight. This is a good moment to stress one of the golden rules: do as much as possible on the ground before take-off, including sharpening your pencils. The fullest marking of a map, close study of high ground, landmarks, railways, etc., notes of distances, expected times, anything in fact which will be of the slightest help when airborne is better done in the unhurried atmosphere of the briefing room. Your Flying Instructor will corroborate this business of never rushing into the air – listen to his eternal nagging about pre-flight checks on the aeroplane for a start.

We wish to measure the Track we are to fly, in this case the Great Circle with apparently no problem. Track is the actual path you intend to follow, or are following, with regard to the ground. Its direction is measured through 360 degrees round the clock, the starting point being the geographical North Pole, or True North as it is usually called. This True North direction is indicated by all the meridians running up your chart from the bottom to the top (yes, that's so even in the southern hemisphere!). Thus, when the North point of the protractor is lined up with a meridian, and the centre point of the protractor is over the Track line, the Track angle is read off at once on the protractor where the Track cuts its edge. This is Track True, since it is measured with reference to True North. Incidentally, there is no way of measuring a Track Magnetic; it has to be calculated.

But there is a snag to our present task. On the Earth and on these maps, the meridians of longitude are parallel to each other only at the Equator, and then they start to converge on each other until they join at the Poles. An angle measured at the meridian of the departure point will thus differ from the angle measured at the destination, for a chosen Track. See Fig. 4.5. The difference on large scale charts is small, but on small charts it can be considerable, demanding the separation of a long Track into a number of sectors for individual measurement. All Tracks on such charts should therefore be measured at the mid-meridian through which the Track passes. The centre point of the Douglas protractor should be placed over the mid-meridian/Track crossing point, the North arrow straight up the meridian, and the Track angle read off on the outside where it lines up with the direction of proposed flight. This is the mean Great Circle (GC) Track in degrees True, from 000° to 359°.

The measurement of distance is relatively simple. The meridians are marked off from time to time into minutes of latitude, as you can see, and a minute of latitude is 1 nm. The dividers are set to span a convenient distance, say 20 nm, and are counted over the Track to give the total distance from departure to destination. It is advisable, again, to use a span taken from an area of latitude around mid-Track, just to get into good habits for the future when other types of charts or smaller scales are used. You can prefer the graduated scale line at the bottom if you like, though in the air you would probably have to unfold the chart, so we plump for the latitude scale at all times.

Try the following trip on the map.

5047N 0150W to 5123N 0243W

The first difficulty is obvious, a swamping of details of lat and long divisions by a heap of topographical matter. A long ruler and dividers may be necessary to line in the latitude and the longitude of the required position, Recheck. It is BOURNEMOUTH aerodrome. Repeat the process with the destination field – BRISTOL. Recheck, and forgive the repetition – the latitude count is towards the North, the longitude towards the West. Join the two points, and mark on this Track a double arrow in the direction of flight, the conventional sign for Track. Take the protractor, centre spot about mid-Track, say 5300N, line up with the meridians (the protractor is squared for this purpose), and read off the Track angle 317°; this is noted as Tr 317(T), the accepted shortened form for Track 317° True, referring to the True North Pole. The degree sign is omitted to avoid confusion with a digit. Now with the dividers at a span of 20 nm from 5050 to 5110, roll from BOURNEMOUTH to BRISTOL, twice and a bit over; take the bit to the same place, 5050N, and the total distance rounded off is 49 nm along track. Or use a graduated scale ruler and read off the answer direct.

The basis of the trip is laid. Halves of miles, of angles or of positions in lat and long are rarely used. Glance now at the railways, trunk roads, high ground, towns, cities, airfields, coastlines, not only Track but to ten miles at either side of it. You will notice the high ground in the last part of the flight, and must plan the approach into BRISTOL with the greatest care.

For practice, what is the Track and distance from BRISTOL to EXETER? Do you agree from your map Tr 215(T), distance 47 nm?

Between the wars, airliners at low level bound for Croydon from foreign parts overflew ASHFORD (Kent) to follow the railway line in a generally westerly direction. What is this direction exactly in °T (Fig. 4.2)? Incidentally can you locate a single-track railway on each of Figs. 4.2, 4.3, 4.4?

Rhumb Lines

So far, our concern has been with **mean** GCs, because a Great Circle cuts the meridians on the maps we're using at different angles, since these meridians converge towards the Pole as they do on the Earth. It follows that a line joining two places which cuts these meridians at the same angle must be a curve. Such a line is called a Rhumb Line (RL). It is certainly not the shortest distance between two points, as a glance at Fig. 4.5 will prove, but a Rhumb line Track is often preferred, since alterations of the aircraft's Heading to allow for converging meridians are avoided. There are projections available which include the property of making a RL a straight line. From our point of view, we know that the mean GC Track measured is the same as the RL Track. This you can prove by a study of Fig. 4.5, checking the paragraph again, and keeping the definitions of

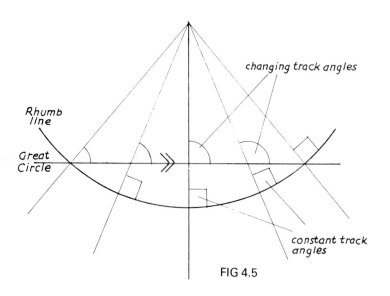

FIG 4.5

GC and RL in your mind. It is quite vital stuff, really, and worth making a song and dance about.

Only at the mid-meridian is the RL and GC Track angle the same. By definition, the RL Track crosses every meridain at the same angle, so there we have it: RL Track and mean GC Track are the same angle, but at any other meridian the GC Track will differ from the constant RL Track.

The RL Track from BOURNEMOUTH to BRISTOL is 317(T), the mean GC Track is also 317(T). The distance measured on our maps is the GC distance, of course, and won't be noticeably different from the RL distance, which would have to be taken from some other projection anyway. There's positively no reason to make a meal of this, but it is enough to keep you going.

Summary

Positions may be plotted from the known Lat and Long of the places. Track is the line between two known positions which the aircraft follows or intends to follow.

60 minutes of Lat or Long is 1°.

One minute of Lat is one nautical mile.

Meridians run from North Pole to South Pole.

Parallels of Latitude are parallel to the Equator.

Rhumb line is the line that cuts every meridian at the same angle.

Great Circle is the shortest distance between two points on the Earth's surface.

Scale is the ratio of chart length to ground distance.

On Lambert's and Transverse Mercator topographical maps, scale may for all practical purposes be taken as correct over the sheet, and a straight line is a GC.

On these charts, a Track measured at its mid-meridian is both the mean GC and a RL.

Track True, Tr(T), is the Track measured with reference to the geographical or True North Pole.

Angles are measured clockwise from 000° to 359°.

A wet afternoon or evening spent carefully reading all the information provided in the margin of the ICAO half-million chart will be time well spent.

5: Directions and speeds

We must now go on to relieve you of the idea, if you ever had it, that to fly from one place to another is simply a case of pointing the aircraft's nose in the direction of the destination and leaving it at that. There are six relevant factors in any flight, three concerned with direction, three with speed. All directions are measured at a meridian, and all speeds are in knots – a knot is one nautical mile per hour. Each of the directions has a speed, so we're in three doubles, really, as follows:

1. The direction of the aircraft's nose in flight, its Heading (Hdg).
   The actual speed of the aircraft in still air, its True Airspeed (TAS).
2. The direction the aircraft is flying with reference to the ground, its Track (Tr).
   The speed of the aircraft over the ground, its Ground speed (G/S).
3. The direction from which the wind is blowing, the wind direction (W/D).
   The speed of the wind (W/S).
   These wind factors are usually put together as wind velocity (W/V), velocity being defined as speed from or in a given direction.

All this lot, Hdg and TAS, Tr and G/S, W/V, determine the movement of the aeroplane when it's airborne. Some are known, decided by the pilot, others are inflicted on him by the caprice of Mother Nature and have to be found by him in flight, so that he knows where he's going and how fast. And knowing any four of the six constituents, a pilot can find the other two, using the information in the planning and navigation of the trip.

Before discussing each individually, we must understand that the wind blows freer away from the Earth's friction, varying in speed and direction with height, and so affecting the aeroplane's direction and speed. Your Track of 317° from BOURNEMOUTH to BRISTOL of the last chapter will not be held in the air if you point the aircraft's nose to 317° in a W/V of 270/40, forty knots from due West; you will be blown well to starboard (right) and finally pass with BRISTOL so far to port (left) that you could miss it entirely.

Heading

This is determined by the pilot, for he sets the direction of his aircraft with his own hands, and (provided the compass is working) he knows about any errors or deviations of the compass, how the Earth's magnetic field is valued in the area, and he can work out the arithmetic of it all; it's not as daunting as it sounds. This is the story.

The Earth is a magnet with a magnetic field of its own. A compass needle which is free to move will point to the Magnetic North Pole, as you learnt in your childhood even if you didn't go to school; or in slightly more adult terms, the needle lines itself up with the magnetic meridian. The Magnetic North Pole is some considerable distance from the True North Pole, and it follows that at any point on the Earth an angle measured on the True meridian will differ from the angle measured at the Magnetic meridian. This angular difference is called **Variation**.

Variation is known and recorded all over the Earth's surface, so the resolution of an angle True into an angle Magnetic is pretty straightforward, but Variation is not constant. The Magnetic North Pole, which is placed about 17° from the True North Pole takes a trip round the True Pole lasting about 960 years. In addition, the whole magnetic field of the globe is affected irregularly by sunspots, and by mineral content in the strata of the Earth's crust. Variation can fortunately be measured worldwide within tolerances quite acceptable for flight, as can the annual changes in all areas. The lines joining all places with equal Variation are called isogonals, and these are certainly not as regular as they appear on the UK maps we've been consulting; in many areas, the isogonals are irregular and complex, with no pattern whatever. To get, say, a Heading True into Magnetic, apply the value of the *mean* isogonal over the area to be flown to the angle measured at the True meridian, and as Variation is noted as so many degrees East or West of the True meridian, here's a diagram or two to clarify matters.

FIG 5.1

In Fig. 5.1 a Variation of say 8° West is shown in (a), and Variation of 10° East in (b); if a Heading of 100(T) is drawn in as in (c) and (d), it will be seen that:

Hdg(T) 100, Variation 8W, then Hdg(M) is 108
and Hdg(T) 100, Variation 10E, then Hdg(M) is 090

It is said that Variation West, Magnetic best
Variation East, Magnetic least

We don't go much on this sort of thing, but must confess that many of our students do; please yourself, after you've finished this chapter.

The annual alteration of Variation is either noted at the base of an isogonal on the chart or in the margin itself. In the UK, it is eight or nine **minutes** annually, taking some years to add up to a whole degree of amendment to the printed value of the isogonal. Naturally, though, one would work to the nearest whole degree, and a chart four years' old or so would call for an increase or decrease of one degree to the tabulated value. For a 10W Variation, with an annual change of 9' East, after four years the Variation would be called 9W; for a Variation of 10W with an annual change of 6' East, the Variation there after 5 years would be 9W, as the Magnetic meridian is apparently moving towards the True Pole reducing the Variation. A Variation of 8E, with an annual change of 8' East would alter the value after 4 years to 9E to the nearest whole degree.

However, we have not quite reached the stage where the pilot can fly off with his compass set to the Heading to steer. The magnetic field of the Earth, measurable and read off a map is one thing; the next and last is the magnetic field of the aircraft itself. This will affect the compass artificially as it were – the Magnetic Heading required will be altered by the magnetic influence of the aircraft (as well as by any built-in errors)

Hdg	100 (T)
Var	4 W
Hdg	104 (M)
Dev	2 W
Hdg	106 (C)

Hdg	100 (T)
Var	7 W
Hdg	107 (M)
Dev	3 E
Hdg	104 (C)

Hdg	100 (T)
Var	24 E
Hdg	076 (M)
Dev	4 W
Hdg	080 (C)

Hdg	100 (T)
Var	16 E
Hdg	084 (M)
Dev	5 E
Hdg	079 (C)

FIG 5.2

which has plenty of permeable metal and electrical circuits. However hard the designers and constructors try, a particular aeroplane will cause the North-seeking end of the compass needle to **deviate** from the actual Magnetic North. And because the needle tries always to align itself with the Magnetic meridian, the effect of these forces varies according to the direction of the aircraft's nose. For example, a piece of iron starboard of the compass bowl will be across the needle on Northerly and Southerly headings, but end on to the needle on Easterly and Westerly. More of this later, though there's no need to go too deeply into it; at this stage, we can be content to state that deviation of the needle of a particular compass in a particular aircraft can be measured and tabulated for the pilot's use and information. Deviation is measured East or West of the **Magnetic** meridian, repeat, the **Magnetic** meridian. An aircraft flying 000(M) may have a compass reading 003(C) – the needle has been pulled 3° to the West by forces in the aircraft, and the deviation would be termed 3°W. To fly the Hdg 000(M) required, the compass in this case has been set to 003(C). An easterly deviation on a particular Heading would demand a lesser Hdg(C), e.g. Hdg 220(M), deviation 4°E, would mean setting 216(C), since the needle has been pulled to the East.

> Deviation West, Compass best
> Deviation East, Compass least

and just how easily can you remember such confounding catch-phrases? Diagrammatically, it's all set out in Fig. 5.2.

Instead of cluttering up the old brainbox with nursery rhymes, the standard memory aid is C D M V T, (Hdg Compass, Deviation, Hdg Magnetic, Variation, Hdg True) Cadbury's Dairy Milk Very Tasty. With such a lay-out, working from the Compass, West is always minus and East is always plus. With that aide-memoire before you, check the following examples, and in case of doubt draw a sketch as above.

C	D	M	V	T
312	2W	310	17W	293
049	5E	054	20E	074
195	4W	191	16E	207
244	3E	247	34W	213

It is imperative that you get this taped; we've known professionals who've got it wrong – 20° Variation wrongly applied means an error of 40° in the Hdg(M) being steered and, happening as in truth it did between the Azores and Barbados, that's an awful lot of water; once, over the desert, the end result was most unacceptable to the fare paying passengers who spent many hours in the eternal sands under the unforgiving sun.

True Airspeed (TAS)

This is latched indisputedly to the Heading. It is the speed through the air, free of outside effects like the wind, but taking into account the composition of the air the thing is flying in. From the cockpit, then, the pilot can select his Heading, and his TAS, but to get the latter he will have to know something of the atmosphere around the aircraft. By this time, you are ready to be told that it's not just a straight reading of an instrument on the panel; you expect a packet of corrections, of course, and they've not altered since Wilbur Wright started it all, simply easier to work out.

From the Airspeed Indicator (ASI) described in Chapter 8, the pilot reads off an Indicated Airspeed (IAS). Now all instruments have some built-in errors, usually minor, which can be measured and tabulated on a card near the instrument for the pilot's information, and the ASI is no exception. The pointer may be a knot or two in error, indicating 2 kt when at rest for example, demanding a correction of −2 kt in flight. Such a case is just Instrument Error. Further, the ASI works by comparing the pressure of air forced into a tube by the aircraft's speed through the air with the static pressure of the surrounding air, but the pressure head (a couple of tubes outside and in front of the airplane) may not be correctly aligned with the airflow, or may be affected by eddies as speed varies, or as the pilot manoeuvres, and so on. Such discrepancies can be measured for the aircraft type at the testing stage and tabulated as Position Error. These two, Instrument Error and Position Error are usually combined into one for a final correction at several indicated speeds on a Pressure Error card (PE). Thus, from the Indicated Airspeed (IAS) read off, the PE is applied to give the Rectified Airspeed (RAS). And, for all that, we have still not got the actual speed the aircraft is making.

There was a mention in the last paragraph of the pressure head, air building up in a tube and so on. Now, the density of the air thins dramatically as height is increased, and the pressure built up in that open-ended tube for a given speed will be lower at height, giving an incorrect reading on the instrument. And to add to our troubles, air density has no standard rate of decrease with height; it depends on pressure and temperature which are very variable factors indeed. Each can, however, be found in flight or forecast before take-off. Pressure can be read on the altimeter in terms of height, which uses a rough standard of pressure decrease with height to give a reading in feet – it is nothing but a barometer, in fact – and the outside, or ambient, temperature can be read from the thermometer (in degrees Celsius, and this will of course have its own private correction card). From there, the height and temperature are taken to the navigation computer together with the RAS and the TAS solved. How this is done is explained in the chapter on the computer.

Track

The path which an aircraft flies with reference to the ground is its Track. The wind has acted on the chosen Heading and blown it on to a Track. How much off the Heading depends on the direction and strength of the wind. A wind from the port side of the aircraft will push it to starboard of the Heading set, and the aircraft's Track will be crabwise. The angular difference between Heading and Track is called **Drift**. A Hdg of 247(T) with a Track of 242(T) means that the wind is blowing in such a way as to cause a drift of 5° Port (5P). A few samples:

Hdg (T)	Tr (T)	Drift
121	125	4S
208	206	2P
004	359	5P
356	003	7S

Drift is always measured from the Heading in degrees port or starboard, and as Track comes straight off the map, magnetic and compass aren't involved, so the step is nearly always done along with True Heading and True Track. The drift would be the same, of course, if you do need Track Magnetic, provided you use Heading Magnetic, e.g., on a leg where the Variation is 7W:

Hdg 294(T)	Track 290(T)	Drift 4P
Hdg 301(M)	Track 297(M)	Drift 4P

Ground Speed

This goes nicely with Track. It is the speed the aircraft is making over the ground and is the result of the wind on the TAS. With a TAS of 200 kt being pushed out by the engines in the teeth of a headwind of 40 kt at your height the G/S is 160 kt. If such a wind were astern the G/S would be 240 kt.

Wind Velocity

This is the speed of the wind from a given direction. It acts on the aircraft's Heading and TAS to give Track and Ground Speed. It is always given True. At the flight planning stage the pilot knows the Track he wants to fly between two places; he decides the height to fly and, with the temperature forecast for this height, he can find his TAS (for he knows his RAS), as a fair estimate; the W/V is forecast. Thus, he has four parts of six, and he can solve the Heading to steer and the expected G/S. From there, he can get the Hdg(M) and Hdg(C), and the time the trip will take.

To plan a trip

1. From the map, measure the Tr(T).
2. Select a height to fly, and from the forecast temperature calculate the TAS from the known RAS.
3. For that height, get the forecast W/V.
4. On the computer, work out the Hdg(T) and the G/S.

5. From the distance of the Track and the G/S, how long will the trip take?

6. On the map, read off the mean isogonal for the trip, or for the first part of the trip if it's a longish one, and get Hdg(M) by applying Variation to Hdg(T).

7. In the aircraft, determine the Hdg(C) from the deviation card near the compass.

8. Decide the estimated time (ETD) of setting Heading(S/H), add on the time the whole flight is expected to take to the destination, and give the Estimated Time of Arrival (ETA) to Control.

The first steps of a safe flight have been taken – a careful, unhurried Flight Plan, and information of your plans given to Control.

Diagrammatically, these factors can be illustrated in what is known as the Triangle of Velocities. You're not too concerned with the theory, so one diagram (Fig. 5.3) will do, as it's all done on the navigation computer before and in flight.

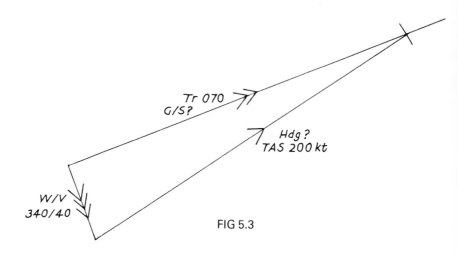

FIG 5.3

Speeds are for one hour, and a scale is chosen. Track is drawn in first, then the W/V; from the end of the W/V vector, the radius of 200 kt TAS is used to strike an arc on Track. The triangle is complete, and Heading 059, G/S just short of 200 kt, say 198 kt, can be measured off. The rule is that the wind and Heading arrows must follow each other – but it's outside the scope of the PPL, and we have books on the market for those wishing to go for higher qualifications.

6: The navigation computer

IBM has nothing to do with it, for our computer is very nearly a pocket instrument and costs only a few pounds. Its operation is something you must get absolutely taped, but with the last chapter absorbed, only perseverance is required. We depart in this section then from cheerful chat into straightforward instruction, you with a computer at the ready.

A word before you buy: we don't advise the waistcoat-pocket size. A model with an overall length of about 10 inches is preferable, and Airtour International, Aristo and Jeppesen sell good sorts, and we're getting no commission from any of them as yet. Don't have anything to do with plastic cursors, either; they break off, usually at the top of climb. Computers are mass-produced, so before passing over the cash, check your choice for serviceability, free rotation of the circles, centre spot dead central on the middle drift line; also, take a model that goes up to 700 kt on the window side, and with Mach number and SG on the slide rule side. A typical example is shown in Figs 6.1 and 6.2, which comes with an instructional handbook in its case.

The instrument is two-fold, a circular slide rule on one side with a number of refinements specific to the airman, while the other side solves the triangle of velocities we've just been talking about. A movable slide fits between them, marked in speeds and drift lines; actually, it is the triangle with only its cogent portion visible.

The Circular Slide Rule

Sometimes called the Appleyard scale, and your guess is as good as ours. Note that the divisions between numbers on both circles are not equidistant, nor do these divisions represent a constant value. When, say, a figure 9 means 9 000, then you will see at a glance that 9 650 needs careful counting. In the case of the figures round the edges, the outer immovable ring is distance, the inner movable scale is time; a general rule and the way the instrument will be most used. You can see that 60 on the inner scale is blacked in with a heavy arrow, and fixing this scale as minutes of time, we can proceed at once to its use.

1. Speed known, distance known, how long?

Speed 200 kt, 140 nm to go. Put the 60 arrow under the 20 on the outer scale, and a speed of 200 nm per hour, 200 kt, has been set up. Read off on the inner (time) scale against 14 on the outer (distance) scale; this 14 means 140 nm, and count the divisions. Is the answer 4.2, 42, 420, 4 200? In this case, for sure, it is 42 minutes and there is rarely any doubt.

FIG 6.1

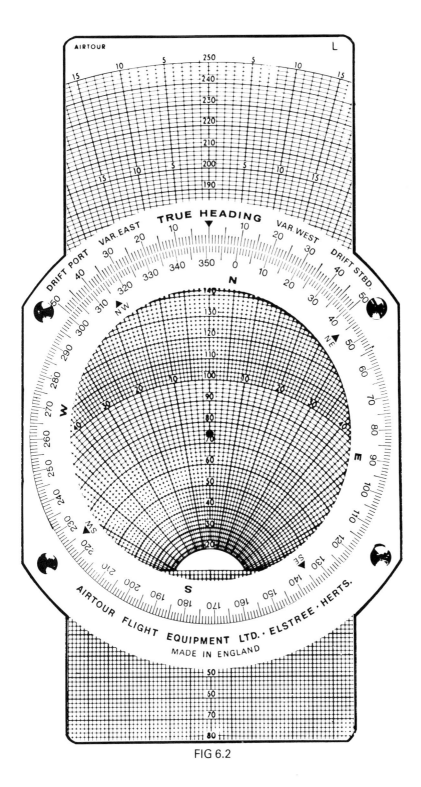

FIG 6.2

Another: speed 155 kt, distance 222 nm. The 60 arrow under 155 on the outer, the divisions 15 to 16 are in fifths, so it's bang in the middle between the second and third marks. Read off on the inner against 222 on the outer. Do you read 86 minutes, which you note as 1 hr 26 min? Even that powerful piece of arithmetic into hours and minutes is done for you if you look.

2. Speed known, time known, how far?

Speed 145 kt, 33 minutes. Place 60 arrow under 145, and read off on the outer (distance) scale against 33 on the inner (time) scale. Answer 80 nm.

Speed 193 kt, 1 hr 07 min. Put 60 arrow under 193, read off on the outer against 67 on the inner. This is 216 nm just. The inner scale is all minutes, so hours and minutes must be turned into minutes before attempting to solve your problem.

One more: speed 99 kt, time 33 min. Set 60 arrow against 99 on the outer, read off on the outer against 33 on the inner; it's a clear $54\frac{1}{2}$, call it 55 nm, to which it is just very slightly nearer. Already, an expertise is being acquired.

3. Distance gone in a known time, what speed?

The distance between two pinpoints in flights is 74 nm, and the time taken is 40 min. Set 40 on the inner scale against 74 on the outer, and read off on the outer against the 60 on the inner; answer 111 kt.

Again, 58 nm in 32 min. Speed is 109 kt

The slide rule with the time element on the movable circle is not restricted to problems such as these with distance: the outer scale can represent fuel, for instance, and the method of solution is unaltered.

4. Fuel consumption known, time known, how much fuel?

Fuel consumption 35 gallons per hour, flight plan time 2 hr 37 min, how much fuel required exclusive of reserves? As before, set 60 on inner scale against 35 on the outer, read off on the outer against 157 minutes on the inner, answer $91\frac{1}{2}$ gallons.

Again, fuel consumption 410 pounds per hour (lb/hr), time 1 hr 21 min, how much fuel exclusive of reserves? 60 on inner scale against 410 on the outer, read off on outer against 81 min on the inner: this gives 554 lb – you will notice a spot of care is needed in this reading.

And really we'd better get up to date and work in the more usually accepted units: consumption 185 kilograms per hour (kg/hr), time 1 hr 12 min, how much fuel? Proceed as before to extract 222 kg.

As a rider, if you have 120 kg left in the tanks at this consumption of 185 kg/hr, you have 39 minutes safe endurance; set the 60 against 185 as before, and this time read off against 120 on the outer the time of 39 min on the inner.

Fuel consumption in level flight can be checked as in note 3 above; say in 28 min you used 108 kg, then the consumption is 232 kg/hr at that power setting. Check?

In all these problems, the inner scale is exclusively used for time, the outer for distance, fuel or whatever is required.

5. Multiplication and division

This is not a terribly popular usage among airmen, but as the thing is a slide rule, we feel it should be mentioned, just for reference.

To multiply 147 by 395, place the 10 (contained in a square on most models) of the inner scale against 395 on the outer, and read off 58 000 on the outer against 147 on the inner. The snag at once is how many noughts in the answer and is the answer exact enough? A mental check for the noughts (here 200 by 400) can be tedious, the precise answer is 58 065, and the error is really too large. This accounts for a preference for doing the sum on a scrap of paper or a pocket calculator, and it is not a frequent turn-up anyway.

To divide 9 712 by 46, place 46 on the inner against 9 712 on the outer, and read off on the outer against 10 on the inner, giving 211; the problems of accuracy remain. That's enough, we've not put it in as a vital contribution to your PPL, but for interest only.

6. Conversion

Here we have a day-to-day activity, and an essential part of your Licence syllabus.

Round the outer ring, you will see sm, nm, km; yards, feet, metres; imperial gallons, US gallons, litres; pounds and kilograms. These may of course be abbreviated and, unfortunately, not always into the generally accepted shortened forms, which we list in an Appendix.

The pilot is plagued by the variety of units in use. Runway lengths may be given in feet, but visibility in km and metres; he may order 50 gallons of fuel, and find 50 US gallons has been poured in, diddling him of $8\frac{1}{2}$ imperial gallons. We've already spoken of the diversity of units used for the heights of obstacles, etc., on maps; an errand of mercy of 100 nm is reported to the Press as 115 miles – the populace understand statute miles and it sounds further anyway. The actual conversions follow; there's no need to memorise them, but do get an idea of the proportion for the purpose of mental checking in large numbers: a kilogram is just over 2 pounds for example, a statute mile is rather less than a nautical mile, a kilometre is about half a nautical mile, a litre is about a fifth of an imperial gallon, and so on.

1 nm is 1·152 sm, 1·852 km
1 km is 0·621 sm, 0·540 nm

To convert nm to sm, multiply by 1·1515
  nm to km, multiply by 1·852
  km to sm, multiply by 0·62137
 1 m is 1·094 yds, 3·281 ft
To convert ft to m, multiply by 0·3048
  m to ft, multiply by 3·2808
  1 US gallon is 0·83 imp gallons, 3·79 litres
  1 imp gallon is 1·205 US gallons, 4·546 litres
To convert imp gall to US gall, multiply by 1·205
  US gall to imp gall, multiply by 0·83
  imp gall to litres, multiply by 4·546
  litres to imp gall, multiply by 0·2205
 1 kg is 2·205 lb
 1 lb is 0·454 kg, and conversion one to the other follows without further ado.

For goodness sake, don't go switching from volume (gallons and litres) into weight (kg and lb). The weight of a gallon of fuel alters with temperature, and this involves a study of specific gravity, not at all pertinent to our present concern (if your curiosity is aroused, the matter is fully explained in our book for CPL and ATPL students 'Ground Studies for Pilots').

All conversions are readily done on the computer, one of its great values; simply turn the given figure on the inner scale to the indicator on the outer and read off the answer against the indicator required. For example, to change 55 lb to kg, turn 55 on the inner to the lb marker on the outer and read off 25 kg on the inner against the kg marker.

71 imp gall is 85 US gall
110 ft is 36½ yd, 33½ m
195 nm is 224 sm, 361 km

Check the items in the conversion table above to familiarise yourself with it all; it is important.

7. To find TAS

Still on the slide rule side, you will see a window marked 'Airspeed'. With the correct factors set in the window, the TAS can be found on the outer ring against the RAS on the inner. The immovable part of the window is pressure altitude, PA, in thousands of feet; this is the aircraft's height with the sub-scale of the altimeter set to 1 013·2 mb, the standard pressure at mean sea level. The figures etched on the moving part round the window are the corrected air temperature in degrees Centigrade at height. By lining up these two factors, the computer is in effect working out the prevailing density of the air in which the aircraft is flying, or plans to fly, and coming up with the TAS. A few examples:

PA 7 000 ft, temp −10°C, RAS 106 kt. With great regard for − or +, set 7(000) against −10, and on the old outer scale, read off against 106 on the inner, the TAS 115 kt.

PA 6 000 ft, temp +3, RAS 115 kt. Set 6(000) against +3°C at the window, read off against 115 on the inner scale the TAS 125 kt on the outer. This temperature is very nearly the standard temperature at 6 000 ft (remember, +15°C at mean sea level decreasing by 1·98°C per 1 000 ft?), but due to the alteration in density, the RAS by no means equals the TAS. This can only happen in standard conditions at mean sea level itself: nought feet, +15°C. Check this on your computer.

One more: PA 40 000 ft, temp −60°C, RAS 156 kt. Proceed as before and you come up with a TAS of 305 kt, nearly double the RAS, the density of the air being so reduced that its resistance to the aircraft's forward thrust is half that at mean sea level.

8. To find True altitude

Very much the same again, using the altitude window. This method on the computer is fairly infrequent, as there are more practical solutions straight from the altimeter itself. We show it now so that you can prove to yourself that indicated altitude is the same as true altitude if conditions are standard, because in effect the altimeter is just a barometer. For example, PA 5 000 ft, temp +5°C; the inner scale 5 000 gives true altitude 5 000 on the outer. Such conditions are rare, of course, so a couple of other examples:

PA 5 000 ft, temp −20°C, read true altitude 4 570 ft

PA 12 000 ft, temp +3°C, gives true altitude 12 500 ft, and you need eyes like a hawk to read it.

All other jollity on this face of the instrument can be left till you strike out beyond the confines of the PPL, but a useful fixed conversion table from °Centigrade to °Fahrenheit and vice versa is usually placed somewhere on the computer. The rule, for what it's worth, to get to F from C is multiply by $\frac{9}{5}$ and add 32; to convert F to C, subtract 32 and multiply by $\frac{5}{9}$. The handy memory tag is 15°C is 59°F. You can check one or two if you like.

The purpose of the computer is to avoid mental activity in the air and speed things up in flight preparation on the ground; it will be at hand all the time, yea, in the examination room as well.

The Navigation Side

Here all problems involving the triangle of velocities are immediately solved. You will recall that of the six factors in flight, Heading and TAS, Track and Ground speed, W/V (wind direction and wind speed), any two unknowns can be found provided the other four are known.

On this side of the computer, the fixed points are the True Heading arrow at the top, and the TAS dot in the centre of the perspex. This is in fact the True Heading and TAS vector of the old triangle of velocities, and with that said we hope to avoid any further theorising. Never forget, though, that when seeking a Track or a Heading, the Heading must finish on its arrow, a point we shall for sure mention again.

The ring turns through 360°; the slide moves up and down, to give a speed figure not only on the centre line but on the arcs on which the speed is marked. The straight graph bit at the base of the slide need not concern you at this moment. The straight lines fanning out from the bottom to the top are drift lines. And should you turn the slide over to deal with higher speeds, for heaven's sake watch it – the scale of the speed markers is quite different. On either side of the True Heading arrow are divisions of degrees of drift Port, to the left and Starboard, to the right. If yours has Var East and Var West provided as well, ignore them. Now all that's required is a pencil and an eraser or wet finger.

1. To find Track and Ground speed

The W/V, Heading and TAS are known. You are flying on a Hdg 250(T), TAS 150 kt, and the W/V, real or forecast, is 300/30, what is Tr and G/S?

First, the W/V must be marked on the perspex. Turn the circle to 300 at the True Heading arrow; then move the slide until any convenient speed is beneath the centre dot, count to 30 below it, and make a pencil cross. For example, if you have put 150 beneath the dot, make the cross on the centre line at 120. This is the W/V of 300/30.

Move the ring until the Hdg 250(T) is in its proper place at the True Heading arrow.

Move the slide until the TAS 150 kt is beneath the centre dot. The four known factors are now shown, Hdg and TAS, W/V. The W/V cross has moved out to the 10° drift line, on the port side, on the speed arc marked 133 kt. The readings can now be taken: Hdg on the centre line 250(T), drift 10P, therefore Track is 240(T). TAS under centre dot 150 kt, G/S under the wind dot 133 kt. The triangle has been solved in 7 seconds flat.

Another: Hdg 218(T), TAS 110 kt, W/V 090/20. Put W/V in first, 090 against the True Heading arrow, 20 kt counted down from the centre spot and marked with a cross. The Hdg 218 can now be put at the True Heading arrow and the slide moved to get 110 kt beneath the centre dot. The wind cross is now on the 7° starboard drift line, so the Track is 225(T) and the G/S is 122 kt. Drift is always measured from Heading, of course.

Say Hdg 170(T), TAS 145 kt, W/V 350/15. Wind in first – 350 against the True Heading arrow, 15 counted down from the centre spot, mark with a cross. The Hdg 170 at the True Heading arrow, TAS 145 under the centre spot. All complete, read off drift nil, so Track is 170, but G/S 160 kt. The wind is dead behind the aircraft, giving a tailwind component of 15 kt.

Last of this type, Hdg 030(T), TAS 180 kt, W/V 120/15. The Track is 025(T), as we read a drift of 5P, and the G/S 180 kt, the wind in this case lightly on the beam.

2. To find Heading and G/S

The Track, W/V and TAS are known, This is the problem in constant use in flight planning and the most trappy.

Let's say a pilot is planning a trip, and has collected the met. forecast. He has agreed a height to fly and, from the weather forecast, he has the expected temperature and W/V for that height. At once, the pilot can work out the TAS he should get. On the map, the Track is drawn in and measured. Four components of the six are now available, and he needs to find the Heading to steer to hold that Track and the speed he will make over the ground while on Track. Keep the relationship clear – Hdg and TAS, Tr and G/S, W/V. He wants the Heading, knows the TAS (albeit from forecast data), knows the Track, wants the G/S and has a forecast W/V.

Off we go, Tr 242(T), W/V 110/30, TAS 150 kt. Proceed to enter the W/V as before, 110 against the True Heading arrow, count 30 down from the centre dot, mark with a cross: W/V 110/30 is plotted. Place TAS 150 under centre dot. Now turn the circle until Track 242 is at the True Heading arrow. The job is not, repeat not, finished, for the Heading must be at the arrow; that arrow, centre drift line and centre spot represent the Hdg and TAS vector of the triangle of velocities. A little fiddling is needed; check the drift as shown by the wind cross 7°S; but drift is calculated from Heading, so turn the circular scale 7° to starboard, to the right. The reading under the Heading arrow is now 235. The wind cross has moved to the 8°S drift line, however, indicating that on a Heading of 235 with this wind, a Track would be made good of 243. The Track we're interested in is 242, so the circle must be moved to 234: the displace-ment of the circle at the arrow must equal the drift shown by the wind cross on the perspex. We have arrived at the situation in the preceding paragraph – all is lined up correctly, and the Heading 234(T) can be entered with the G/S of 169 kt under the cross on the drift line of 8S.

The juggling required does demand a full understanding of the difference between Hdg and Tr. Half degrees and an odd knot are immaterial, of course, but with a strong wind on the beam the juddling can be consider-able. At all costs, ensure that it's the Heading that is at the arrow before taking the final reading, and that the degrees moved there agree with the degrees of drift shown on the drift lines.

Let's try a few more examples:

Tr 324, W/V 230/20, TAS 137 kt. Mark in W/V, 230 against the True Heading arrow, 20 counted down from the centre dot. Place TAS 137 under centre dot. Turn Tr 324 to the TH arrow. Drift is apparently 9S. Allow for this by turning the circle so that a Hdg of 315 is at the TH arrow. The wind cross has scarcely moved from 9S in this movement, so the operation is complete – Hdg 315(T), drift 9S will give the wanted Tr 324(T), and the G/S reads 136 or 137 under the wind cross.

Tr 001, TAS 192 kt, W/V 070/40. Enter the wind cross, shove the slide up till TAS 192 is under the centre dot, turn Tr 001 to the TH arrow: drift appears to be 12P. Allow for this by turning the circle until 013 is at the TH arrow. This Heading has moved the wind cross to 11P drift line, so adjust by turning the circle to 012 at the TH arrow. All complete – Hdg 012(T), drift 11P, so Tr 001 as required, and G/S on this Track is 174 kt as shown under the wind cross.

Keep going: Tr 184, W/V 350/25. TAS 169 kt. Enter wind cross, TAS under centre dot, Tr 184 at the TH arrow, and watch the slide doesn't budge. Read 2P drift. Allow by turning 186 to the arrow as a trial Hdg; there is no real movement of the wind cross on the drift lines, so all is done. Hdg 186(T), drift 2P gives the required Tr 184(T), and the G/S is 193 kt.

Last one: Tr 068, W/V 200/40, TAS 350 kt. Mark in the W/V cross, slide 350 under the centre dot. Lo, the slide must be extracted and turned over, and the wind cross re-entered as the scale now jumps in tens. Re-enter 200/40. TAS 350 under centre dot, Tr 068 at the TH arrow, and read drift 5P. Adjust circle to give a Hdg 073 to allow for 5° port drift; the wind cross has not moved from the 5P drift line so Hdg 073, drift 5P, Tr 068, and G/S 376 kt.

The usual error in the fiddling is turning the circle the wrong way in the first step in assessing drift. Always check mentally that **drift is applied to Heading** – Hdg 073, drift 5P, Tr 068.

3. To find W/V

The Hdg, TAS, Tr and G/S are known. An aircraft is on a Heading of 050(T), TAS 160 kt; from a pinpoint after half an hour's flying, the pilot reckons he has made good a Track of 059(T), and his speed over the ground has been 140 kt. He can now find the wind that is actually blowing, and compare it with the forecast. The computer work is simple, and relates with what we have already done. Set Hdg 050 against the TH arrow, and the TAS 160 under the centre spot. No more movement of the circle is needed, for the centre line is complete. If track is 059, then with this Heading, drift is 9S; G/S has been calculated in flight to be 140 kt, so where the 9S drift line crosses the 140 kt arc make a mark on the perspex, the usual cross. Turn this cross till it is below the centre spot on the centre line. Read off against the TH arrow a wind direction of 004, call it 005, and count down from the centre spot a speed of 31, call it 30. The W/V is 005/30, give or take a little, for the wind just does not blow steadily in direction or speed.

Hdg 333(T), TAS 122, Tr 329(T), G/S 141 kt. Set Hdg 333 against TH arrow, TAS 122, under centre dot. Where drift 4P crosses the 141 speed arc make a cross, which is now turned below the dot on the centre line. Read wind direction (W/D) 125, and wind speed (W/S) 22, noted as W/V 125/22 in the accepted terminology.

Hdg 074, TAS 130, Tr 083, G/S 130, gives W/V 348/20, check.

Lastly, to use both sides of the computer – an aircraft is on Hdg 134(T), RAS 120 kt, pressure altitude 5 000 ft, temperature +6°C, and makes good a Track of 130(T) between two pinpoints 57 nm apart in 31 min. What is the W/V?

On the circular slide rule, find the TAS by entering the Airspeed window with PA 5(000) and temp 6°C, reading off on the outer scale against RAS 120 on the inner, giving a TAS of 129 kt. Heading and TAS are ready. Now for G/S: 31 minutes on the inner scale against 57 nm on the outer gives G/S 110 kt on the outer scale against the inner scale 60. Track and G/S speed are ready. Over to the navigation side of the computer: Hdg 134 against TH arrow, TAS 129 under the centre dot; Tr 130 means drift 4P, so mark at the 4P drift line on the 110 speed arc; turn to the centre line under the dot, and read off a W/V 156/20.

4. To find Wind Component

The squared graticule on the computer slide can be used to find wind components. For example, if the wind is 045/40, what are the wind components along and across runway 35? The W/V of course is in °T and the runway is in °M, so convert the runway direction 350°M to °T. Assume in this case variation is 5°W so the runway is 345°T.

Enter the W/V 045 against the True Heading Index as usual. Adjust the slide to 0 at the top of the squared graticule and mark downwards the W/V cross at 40 kt. Rotate the circle until 345° is against the True heading Index. Read off the Headwind Component of 20 kt and the Cross-wind Component of 35 kt to Port.

A brisk familiarity with the computer is paramount in easing the pilot load, and we've already mentioned that this chapter is in the nature of a hard grind, so we've put in a series of exercises to end with. And don't forget, the PPL exam contains plenty of sums for the computer. At least, every thing on it is practical, and competence in its use does make for easier flying.

Some sums on the computer:

Fill in the blanks:

	Hdg	TAS	W/V	Tr	G/S
1.	220	115	315/30		
2.	003	120		359	132
3.		172	240/40	085	
4.		154	180/25	166	
5.	301	160		308	145
6.	147	105	270/20		

Find the TAS:

	Pressure alt ft	Temp °C	RAS kt
7.	5 000	+3	100
8.	8 500	0	125
9.	9 000	−7	106
10.	3 500	+10	110

Convert:
11.   275 km to nm.
12.   520 m to ft.
13.   109 Imp gal to US gal.
14.   157 kg to lb.
15.   435 litres to Imp gal.

Give speed in kt:
16.   49 nm in 19 min.
17.   103 km in 22 min.
18.   157 sm in 37 min.

At 167 kt:
19.   time to fly 140 km?
20.   time to fly 200 sm?
21.   how many km flown in 44 min?
22.   how many sm flown in 51 min?
23.   A mountain peak is 4 230 m amsl. What height in ft amsl must be flown to clear it by 3 000 ft?
24.   How much fuel is required for a flight of 295 nm, G/S 124 kt, consumption 30gal/hr, carrying a reserve of 20 gal?
25.   Your tanks hold 320 kg of fuel, consumption 70 kg/hr, TAS 140 kt, tailwind component +20 kt, you wish to keep 50 kg in reserve. What ground distance can you cover in flight?
26.   An aircraft's consumption is 25 gal/hr, and Heading is set with fuel for 2 hr 50 min. How much is left in the tanks after flying 200 nm at a mean G/S of 130 kt?
27.   Flight distance is 250 nm from A to B, consumption 120 kg/hr, the tanks hold 350 kg. What G/S must be averaged to arrive over B with 50 kg left on board?

Answers

1. Tr205, G/S 122	10. 116 kt	19. 27 min
2. W/V 145/15	11. 148½ nm	20. 1 hr 02½
3. Hdg 091, G/S 208	12. 1 705 ft	21. 226 km
4. Hdg 168, G/S 130	13. 131 US gal	22. 163 sm
5. W/V 250/25	14. 346 lb	23. 16 900 ft
6. Tr 139, G/S 117	15. 95½ Imp gal	24. 91½ gal
7. 107 kt	16. 155 kt	25. 618 nm
8. 142 kt	17. 152 kt	26. 33 gal
9. 120 kt	18. 222 kt	27. 100 kt

7: A spot of navigation

Despite all the planning in the world a trip will rarely work out as expected, and blaming the forecaster when you find yourself off Track doesn't bring you back on. Positive action must be taken, and this doesn't demand a packet of theory, maps or navigation equipment; constant alertness plus a few simple principles will turn an amateurish sortie into a safe, well-rounded flight.

During your flying training you will have had plenty of dual and solo practice in finding your way round the country with the help of a topographical map. All the tricks of map reading, as well as the pitfalls, will have been impressed on you continually and often coarsely by your flying instructor, who for sure didn't let you loose on a solo cross-country unless he was satisfied that you'd acquired a reasonable competence. The next step is to get beyond the stage of just reaching your destination. Some skill in altering Heading, using Fixes, amending ETAs is needed, and now that you are on your own, flying the aeroplane as well, the method must be crisp.

The 1 in 60 Rule

This little formula is a blessing, providing a handy method of altering Heading without much mental strain, even without using the computer. It has a geometrical base, and makes a pleasant change from the fustian of your business life. Specifically, if an aircraft is 1 nm off Track after flying 60 nm, the Track error is 1°. See Fig. 7.1.

FIG 7.1

The Track planned is AB, distance 60 nm, but if instead of flying over B, the pilot pinpoints himself over C, 1 nm to the side, then the Track error is 1°. It's all approximate, but within reason (that is, a Track error of up to 20°) it works well enough. From this, it follows that $\frac{1}{2}$ nm off in 30 nm is also 1° Track error, as is 2 nm off in 120. We're talking about Tracks, remember, Tracks we plan to fly and Tracks we make good.

Putting this 1 in 60 relationship into mathematical terms, the formula is:

$$\text{Track Error} = \frac{\text{distance off} \times 60}{\text{distance gone}}$$

Say the distance off is $1\frac{1}{2}$ nm in 60 nm, then

$$\text{Track Error} = \frac{1\frac{1}{2} \times 60}{60} \text{ which is } 1\frac{1}{2}°$$

Again, 2 nm off in 120 nm

$$\text{TE} = \frac{\text{distance off} \times 60}{\text{distance gone}}$$

$$= \frac{2 \times 60}{120}$$

$$= 1°$$

and, 4 nm off in 73 nm

$$\text{TE} = \frac{4 \times 60}{73}$$

$$= 3° \text{ to the nearest degree.}$$

It is quite accurate enough to arrive mentally at the nearest whole degree; an aircraft cannot be flown for long to within 1° anyway, and the aim is to do the sums on the dot.

Last one for the time being, 3 nm off in 48 nm

$$\text{TE} = \frac{3 \times 60}{48}$$

$$= 4°$$

Learn the formula now. There's nothing to prevent you doing the multiplication and division on a pocket calculator or the Appleyard scale as outlined in Chapter 6, of course, but why get the computer out at all?

Now a position, pinpoint or, as we call them all, a Fix, is no use unless it has some value in the navigation of the aircraft. Consider the case of a pilot who wishes to fly from A to B, a distance of 104 nm; he draws the Track on the map, measures it as 224°(T). From the Flight plan, he sets Heading (S/H) 221(T), expecting 3S drift. He gets a Fix 41 nm after setting Heading which is 2 nm to starboard of his required Track. Action stations.

$$\text{TE} = \frac{\text{distance off} \times 60}{41}$$

$$= \frac{2 \times 60}{41}$$

$$= 3°$$

He has, then, on a Heading of 221 actually made good a Track of 227, as near as dammit a drift of 6S. If he'd known when he left A that he would get 6S drift, his Heading would have been 218 to give the Track required 224. An alteration of Heading now to 218 will give Track 224, but it will be parallel to the original one planned. Run through that lot again from Fig. 7.2.

FIG 7.2

Altering by the same amount as the Track error only results in a Track parallel to the original, and more must be done before altering Heading to make the destination airfield. Without boring you to tears with a story about exterior and interior angles of a triangle, the correction to the aircraft's nose must be the Track error plus a further number of degrees dependent on the distance to go. Start with a simple case as shown in Fig. 7.3.

FIG 7.3

In Fig. 7.3, A to B is 120 nm, the Track required. After flying 60 nm, the aircraft is 2 nm to port of this Track. Track error is then 2°. An alteration of 2S would give a parallel Track CE, but a further 2S alteration would bring the aircraft to B. If you did O level maths not too long ago, you could even chat about the properties of isosceles triangles. The track error was 2°, the further correction to get to B, the 'closing angle', was 2°, so the full alteration was 4° starboard of the original course. Now to some more practical examples and the equation for finding closing angle.

Track 090(T), Hdg 091(T), dist A to B 118 nm, and a Fix is obtained at C, 5 nm to port of desired Track after 46 nm flying (Fig. 7.4).

$$\text{At once, TE} = \frac{5 \times 60}{46} = 7°$$

FIG 7.4

Alteration of 7S would give parallel Track CF

$$\text{Closing angle} = \frac{\text{dist off} \times 60}{\text{dist to go}}$$

$$= \frac{5 \times 60}{72} = 4°$$

The complete angle to alter is $7 + 4 = 11°$ to starboard. The Hdg(T) would be amended to 102 in order to make B.

    Should you urgently need to regain the original Track, then just double the Track error and alter Heading (A/H) in the appropriate direction. This will get you back on your original Track in the same distance that you flew to the Fix. The turn on to Track will take the Track error into account. Better flash a picture (Fig. 7.5):

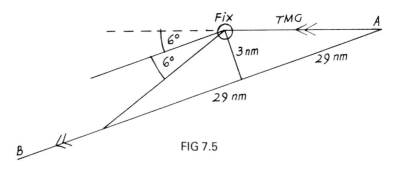

FIG 7.5

A to B 94 nm, Fix 3 nm to starboard after 29 nm.

$$\text{TE} = \frac{3 \times 60}{29} = 6°$$

A/H 12P to regain original Track. On regaining, turn on with a Heading allowing for 6° more starboard drift than was built into the Heading out from A. An advantage of this method of getting on to Track is that the time taken to regain will be just about the same as that taken from A to the Fix – the old isosceles triangle bit.

To sum up:
   Calculate Track error
   To make parallel Track, A/H in opposite direction by amount of Track error.
   To regain original Track, A/H in opposite direction by double the Track error.
   To make destination, A/H in opposite direction by Track error + closing angle.

This last is the usual requirement, but obstructions and high ground, heavy traffic and so on may be the stoppers, so have the rules at your finger tips. It's all part of the constant alertness pattern.

5° and 10° drift lines

As always, as much as possible is done on the ground to help activities in the air. The exercise of the 1 in 60 rule is much eased if lines of drift 5° and 10° are drawn in on both sides of Track on the map in the Briefing Room. When a Fix is obtained, then the drift angle can be estimated, visually, and you have the Track error straight away; you've still got to go through the performance in the summing up above for the amount to alter Heading.

Quick return to Base

Sooner or later, you will set off on a trip and after a while find urgent reasons which demand an immediate return to the departure field. You can work out the Heading to steer while you are doing a 180 with the aircraft. In the simplest case, you've been flying Hdg 245(T) from the Flight plan, hoping to make good a Track of 240(T), expecting that is 5P drift. It is imperative now to make good a reciprocal Track 060(T). An alteration of Heading to reciprocal 065 will give a Track of 070, for the drift is now of course starboard, and we don't need to draw a diagram to illustrate that great truth. It is clear that the new Heading must be 055 to allow for 5° drift starboard. So the rule is: to turn on to reciprocal Track, take reciprocal Heading, and subtract double the drift if it was Port originally, add if it was starboard. Hdg 132(T), Track 139(T), what Hdg(T) to steer to make good Tr 319(T)?

   Drift is 7S
   Reciprocal Hdg 312
   Add   14S
   ─────────────────────────
   Hdg to steer   326(T)

We're talking all the time in terms of Heading True. Don't forget that in the aircraft you will have been steering Hdg(C) and so must make due amendments for variation and deviation. Better do one more: Hdg 003(C), dev 2W, Var 11E, Tr 357(T). What Hdg (C) to steer to make good reciprocal Track, with dev 2E? Sorry, but it is the sort of thing that happens.

C D M V T and West is minus: Hdg 003(C), dev 2W gives 001(M)
Hdg 001(M), Var 11E gives 012(T)
Tr 357(T), Hdg 012(T), drift is then 15P
Reciprocal Hdg   192
Subtract drift   30P

  Hdg to steer $\overline{162(T)}$, Var 11E, Hdg 151(M), dev 2E, Hdg 149(C).

Corrections to ETA

On the Flight plan, using all the information available, the time a trip, or a leg of a trip, will take is written in; on setting Heading (S/H), the expected ETA will be noted for each turning point as well as for the destination. In flight, these ETAs must be checked and if necessary revised, for you are dealing with facts, not forecasts. And if you are wise, arrangements will have been made to let your destination know your ETA even if only by phone from the controller at the departure aerodrome.

An elementary method is to divide up the Track into a number of equal parts, or a variety of parts where recognisable landmarks are placed. When airborne, jot down the ETA thereat on the chart and check the actual arrival time (ATA). If you are a couple of minutes late at the first, then a further couple will be lost on the next equal part, and the final ETA can be adjusted continually throughout the voyage.

To go on with the previous chat about the value of a Fix, the Fix on Track will cause little difficulty in amending an ETA on a single leg, as well as a preliminary amendment to the final one. The circular slide rule comes into its own: after flying for 23 min, a Fix is obtained on Track 45 nm from departure airfield. Whatever the Flight plan says, the G/S is 117 kt; if there is 35 nm to go on that leg, it will most likely take 18 min. To put this into practice, the actual time of departure (ATD) is 1543 hr, and ETA at destination B is calculated at 1652 hr, dist 149 nm. After flying for 19 min a Fix is found on Track 39 nm from A. What is the revised ETA?

> 39 nm in 19 min gives G/S 123 kt
> 110 nm to go at this G/S gives 54 min
> 1543 hr + 19 min + 54 min gives ETA 1656 hr

20 min later a further Fix is obtained, 40 nm from the first. The very latest G/S is thus 120 kt, and there's 70 nm to go: this will, at this G/S, take 35 min, and the new ETA at B is

> 1543 hr + 19 + 20 + 35 min or 1657 hr

In flight, naturally, the arithmetic will be progressively done; do not think of mean G/S either, for you are interested only in the latest, and you can see that even the latest is far from being what you will get for sure on the next piece of the trip; but at least you are aiming for precision with the information available.

In cases when the Fix is off Track, and it usually turns out that way, the new Track should be drawn in and measured as nearly as possible (or assumed if nothing else can be done in the confines of the cockpit) and a G/S worked out for this Track on the computer using the forecast W/V if that's all you've got, or the new W/V calculated by the Track and G/S method at the last Fix. This really is not so rattling hard as it sounds. If you look back at some of the matter we've run over already, it is only a case of doing in the air the stuff on wind finding you've already done in the computer chapter – after having found the Track made good (TMG) and G/S in the way you are accustomed by now.

It's worth recalling that Sir Francis Chichester flew over the Tasman Sea, a rather turbulent area, in a light aircraft by himself, navigating by astro, in the 1930s. All you need are the basic navigation instruments and a map – but don't keep you head in the cockpit for long.

Here are a few sample questions such as may be expected in an examination for a PPL. The topic of 'pilot navigation', as it is known, is pretty important and all tests are bound to have a question or more on it.

1. You are flying from A to B, distance 73 nm, Track 167(T), Hdg 165(T). After flying 20 nm from A on this Heading, you find you are 4 nm to port of Track.
   Give the new Heading to maintain to reach B.
2. An aircraft leaves C at 1244 to fly to D, distance 237 nm. At 1301, the aircraft is on Track, 51 nm from C.
   Give the ETA for D.
3. An aircraft is flying from A to B, distance 150 nm. When 30 nm from A, a Fix is obtained 6 nm to starboard of Track. What alteration must be made to the Heading in order to reach B?
4. An aircraft leaves A at 1017 to get to B 135 nm away. At 1038, the pilot fixes himself 4 nm to port of Track, 40 nm from A, and decides to regain his original Track soonest.
   (i)   What alteration to Heading will he make at once?
   (ii) Give ETA to regain Track.
   (iii) On regaining Track, what further alteration to Heading will he make to reach B?

Answers

1. 181(T)	3. 15P
2. 1403 hr	4. (i) 12S (ii) 1059 hr (iii) 6P

8: Instruments and compasses

The degree of sophistication of your instrument panel will depend upon your aeroplane and your purse but like motor-cars and boats, the range fitted as standard is steadily increasing. From the earliest times, there has been a basic panel designed to furnish the pilot with information on the aircraft's airspeed, its altitude and vertical speed, its attitude, turn and balance and finally its heading (i.e. a magnetic compass). The instruments' operation and interpretation by the pilot is described below – the engine instruments have already been referred to in chapter 3.

1. The Airspeed Indicator (ASI)

A vintage biplane like a Moth can have a very rudimentary indicator fitted to a strut visible from the cockpit comprising a spring leaf which is deflected increasingly further backwards over a scale plate, the faster that the aeroplane goes through the air. However for the non goggles and scarf type, a more sophisticated instrument is provided on the panel in the modern light aeroplane.

On an exposed forward-facing part of the aeroplane (fuselage or main-plane) a pitot, or pressure, head is fitted to sense the air pressure caused by the aircraft's movement. The undisturbed air pressure, called static, is augmented by the dynamic pressure due to the motion to give a total pressure called pitot pressure. The airflow at a pitot-static tube is shown in Fig. 8.1, although some aircraft have a separate sensor for static pressure on the side of the fuselage, called a static vent.

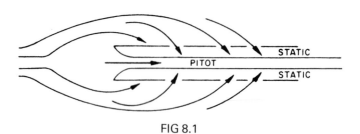

FIG 8.1

From the sources of pitot and static pressure, pipelines are run to the rear of the instrument panel to the Airspeed Indicator (ASI), the construction of which is shown in Fig. 8.2.

Pitot
pressure

Static
pressure

capsule   mechanical   bi-metallic   dial and
            linkage   strip   pointer

FIG 8.2

By feeding pitot pressure to a capsule surrounded by static pressure from the aircraft flight level, increasing capsule movement drives the ASI pointer. However the Indicated Airspeed (IAS) does need correction to get True Airspeed (TAS), although you will find the placarded speeds for handling given in IAS. The corrections arise from:

1. *Instrument Error* – due to any imperfections in manufacture.

2. *Position Error* – due to incorrect pressure being sensed and fed to act on the capsule.

These two are combined on a card (PE card) and applied to the IAS to obtain Rectified Airspeed (RAS).

3. *Density Error* – The ASI is calibrated to read correctly when the air density is equivalent to that found at mean sea level in the International Standard Atmosphere (ISA). When RAS is corrected for the ambient air density, TAS is obtained.

For high speed aircraft, flying at a TAS of 300kt or more, a further correction for Compressibility Error is made to allow for the fact that air brought to rest in the pitot head compresses at high speeds.

Should either or both the pitot and static pressure supplies become blocked, say by ice, then the ASI will read incorrectly, indeed seriously so.

The presentation of IAS to the pilot on the ASI dial depends upon the particular instrument manufacturer but it is common to have speed ranges colour-coded and particular speeds marked so that the pilot can see important airspeeds at a glance. Typically at the lower speeds a white arc spans upwards from the stalling speed, power off in the landing configuration, then a green arc spans up to the maximum speed at which the aircraft can fly in rough air. A yellow arc spans the cautionary speed range and the aircraft can only fly at these airspeeds in smooth air. A red marker at the top end of the yellow range indicates V_{NE} (never exceed speed).

The pilot's pre-flight checks on the ASI are limited. On the external check, the pilot ensures that the pressure head is secure, unblocked and its cover removed. Inside, he checks the operation of the pitot head heater. The ASI is a sealed instrument and the pilot checks that the glass front is not loose or cracked and the pointer is indicating zero, unless facing into a blustery wind.

2. The Altimeter

The atmosphere is constantly exerting pressure on us and the pressure at a particular point and time can be measured by an aneroid barometer, aneroid meaning 'not wet' or 'without liquid'. As an aeroplane ascends, there is less weight of air left above it so the air pressure is reduced. By making certain assumptions, this fall in pressure can be calibrated on the instrument dial as an increase in altitude. The actual sensing of the pressure around the aeroplane is done by a block of capsules, partially evacuated of air and held open by a spring. As shown in Fig. 8.3, as the

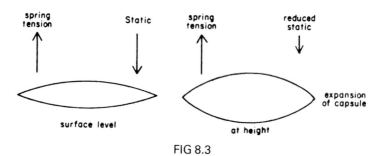

FIG 8.3

aeroplane gains height and the value of air pressure (conveyed through the aircraft's static pressure system) decreases, so the capsules expand under the influence of the spring. A schematic presentation of the construction of an altimeter is shown in Fig. 8.4

The altimeter dial calibration is based on the International Standard Atmosphere (ISA) which assumes:

1. Mean Sea Level – Pressure 1013·25 millibars, temperature +15°C
2. Temperature decreases with height by 1·98C° per 1 000 ft up to 36 090 ft where it is −56·5°C and then remains constant with height at −56·5°C.

The instrument is fitted with a datum setting knob which controls a subscale so that the pilot can read:

Height above aerodrome level
Altitude above mean sea level
Aircraft flight level.

static

leaf
spring

two or more
evacuated
capsules

mechanical
linkage

bi-metallic
strip

FIG 8.4

In the UK, the subscale is calibrated in millibars and the particular settings used are known world-wide by their Q-code names which are dealt with later in chapter 9 – Meteorology. Because of accidents being caused by mis-reading of altimeters, new presentations are being introduced to combat this risk. Generally however altimeters have a pointer indicating 100s of feet so that pilots can immediately sense changes of height.

Apart from mis-setting of the subscale, the errors to which an altimeter is subject are:

1. *Instrument Error* – due to imperfections in manufacture and installation.
2. *Temperature Error* – due to the difference between the actual temperature and ISA temperature in the column of air below the aircraft.
3. *Pressure Error* – due to incorrect pressure being sensed and fed through the static line.
4. *Time-lag Error* – due to the pressure in the static line not changing immediately the aircraft changes the level at which it is flying. In a rapid descent, the altimeter will over-read, and of course if the static vent becomes blocked with ice, the altimeter reading will be incorrect.

The pre-flight check of the pressure head and static vent for the ASI also ensures correct static pressure supply to the altimeter. Again, as a sealed instrument, the glass face must be clear, tight and uncracked. Check that rotating the datum setting knob produces a change in both the subscale reading and the altimeter pointer – more millibars, more feet. Also forward pressure on the setting knob must not disengage the subscale from the altimeter pointer. When set to QFE (or QNH as required) the altimeter should read correctly within a tolerance of +30 to −50 ft.

3. The Vertical Speed Indicator (VSI)

Like the altimeter, the VSI operates from static pressure acting on a capsule. In this case, static pressure is supplied into the capsule. The space in the case around the capsule is also supplied with static pressure but only after it has been delayed by passing through a metering unit. (Fig. 8.5)

FIG 8.5

All the time the aeroplane is cruising at a constant pressure level, the two pressures inside and outside the capsule are the same and the VSI reads 0 climb/descent. As soon as the aeroplane changes height, the new static pressure acts in the capsule while the change in pressure around it is delayed. This differential is then indicated as a rate of climb or descent. Even so, one error of the VSI is that it always lags immediately after a change in flight level. Equally, sudden changes in pitch cause a few moments of fluctuation while a completely iced-up static line makes the instrument useless.

The pre-flight check for the pilot of his VSI also overlaps that for the ASI and the altimeter. As a sealed pressure instrument the glass face must be clear, tight-fitting and uncracked. It should also read zero on the ground!

4. The Attitude Indicator (Artificial Horizon)

There is a whole range of presentations of the dial of this instrument, some in glorious colour. Fig. 8.6 shows a typical instrument face.

FIG 8.6

The instrument has a gyroscope which is rotated at high speed either electrically or by air jets, with its axis mounted vertically. The gyro remains rigid in space while the aircraft manoeuvres about it. A bar at 90° to the gyro rotor axis, indicating the horizon, compares the aircraft attitude with a symbolic aircraft which is part of the instrument case. Typical presentations are shown in Fig. 8.7.

climb with 30°
left bank

climb

climb with 30°
right bank

30° left bank

level

30° right bank

glide with 30°
left bank

glide

glide with 30°
right bank

FIG 8.7

The gyro in the instrument is mounted in gimbals but even so it has some limits to its freedom. Where the facility is available, the gyro should be caged before indulging in aerobatics. The artificial horizon suffers from acceleration and turning errors. The former is most noticeable in take-off conditions. The latter generally occurs in turns in excess of rate one.

5. The Turn and Balance (Slip) Indicator

This indicator is really two instruments in one, showing rate of turn and whether the aircraft is correctly balanced or if there is any skid or slip. The state of balance has two alternative presentations – either by a ball in a curved tube at the bottom of the instrument face (Fig. 8.8) or by a pointer (operated by a pendulous weight) in the upper part of the instrument face (Fig. 8.9).

straight and level   rate 1 left turn – slip   rate 1 left turn – balanced

FIG 8.8

correctly balanced –   rate 2 left turn – slip   rate 1 right turn – skid
left turn rate 2

FIG 8.9

The rate of turn is derived from a spring-restrained gyroscope which operates a pointer over the half of the face not involved with the skid/slip indication.

The instrument is easily checked whilst turning when taxying by noting the turn indication is in the correct direction and that the balance pointer is indicating a skid.

6. The Aircraft Compass

A compass needle, freely suspended, influenced only by the magnetism of the Earth, will line up with the Earth's line of total force at that spot. This brings us trouble at once, for at the Magnetic Poles the lines of force plunge vertically into the Earth's crust, and the compass needle wants to stand upright, a useless property for anyone interested in direction on the surface. In fact, above latitude 70°, the magnetic compass is absolutely no good whatever. Conversely, at the Magnetic Equator, an irregular line roughly equidistant from each Magnetic Pole, the compass will lie precisely horizontal, just what's wanted. Between the Magnetic Pole and Magnetic Equator, the needle will line up with the Earth's line of total force, which may have any combination of vertical and horizontal components in it.

The horizontal component is called Directive force, known as 'H', while the vertical force is just known as 'Z'. At the Magnetic Poles, Z is maximum, H is nil. At any spot except the Magnetic Equator, a freely suspended compass needle will dip from the horizontal (it's actually called 'Dip'), and this is one of the factors which has to be overcome before the compass can be of value to the pilot – he wants the magnetic meridian, the direction in the horizontal only.

Aircraft magnetism

A further series of complications arise from the aircraft itself – a heap of metal, full of electrical circuits and frictional parts. Now some metals are incapable of magnetisation and so are not part of our present thesis; others pick up magnetism easily and lose it easily; others in contrast are difficult to magnetise, and surrender very slowly indeed. There will be some of each in any aircraft, and the easy sort, called 'soft iron', will have magnetism induced in it just by being in the Earth's magnetic field. The hard sort, called 'hard iron', will need some external force to magnetise it, such as hammering and riveting, and there's plenty of that when an aeroplane is on the jigs during construction. Move it away and the soft iron will lose its induced magnetism and assume the different polarity of the new place it's in, but the hard iron firmly retains the polarity it acquired while building.

The effect on the compass is mainly from permanent hard iron magnetism, which can be analysed by checking the compass on known magnetic headings, and recording the differences. These differences are of course deviation and the process of finding deviation is called 'swinging the compass'. Swinging is done on the ground, by a qualified Compass Adjuster, engines on, radios and electric circuits working as far as possible as in flight, for their magnetic effect can be different at rest from their effects in operation. Included at the time of the swing will be the effects of soft iron magnetism, so if the aircraft is flown from an area like the UK where the swing took place to some distance off like Australia, then the value of induced soft iron magnetism will be greatly different. If the aircraft is to operate in the new area, it should be re-swung. Changes in deviation on a long flight are something to be aware of: they are usually caused by Z, the vertical force, inducing magnetism into any soft iron whose upper and lower poles are sufficiently lined up with the compass needle to affect it.

7. The 'P' type (direct reading) compass

Aircraft manufacturers go to great lengths to de-magnetise their products before delivery, getting the magnetic influences to a workable minimum so that they cause the least deviation on the compass. It is impossible to build an aeroplane without the use of some ferrous material; nor can the manufacturer entirely screen the magnetism set up by electric circuits, or the frictional effects of moving parts; and he certainly cannot allow for the different magnetic fields that the aircraft will operate in. The compass constructor can however do a lot to nullify the unwanted elements, such as Dip, and to amplify the desirable such as a steady dead beat needle.

In the UK, the angle of dip from the horizontal is about 66° and this must be got rid of somehow because the pilot wants the needle pointing straight along the magnetic meridian, not towards the centre of the Earth. This is done by making the magnet system pendulous; four short magnets are used in fact, close mounted beneath the pivot. When the Earth's vertical force Z tilts the magnets, the centre of gravity moves out from below the point of suspension bringing a righting force into action. In this way, the tilt due to Z is almost entirely counter-acted by the weight of the magnet system acting through the centre of gravity. It is emphatically *not* a built-in mechanical adjustment, but a displacement of the centre of gravity due to the system's pendulosity, which will take place and correct for Dip whichever end of the needle does the dipping. The needle finishes up only 2° or 3° from the horizontal, until about latitude 70 N or S and beyond, where Z is so strong and H so weak that the magnetic compass is useless.

FIG 8.10

To make the needle sensitive and fixed firmly along the magnetic meridian, its pole strengths are made as strong as possible, the pivot is of iridium in a cup of corundum to keep friction to a minimum, and the lot is suspended in liquid (methyl alcohol) to reduce the effective weight of the system as well as lubricate the pivot. Four short powerful magnets are used, damping filaments are fitted to the system, and with the weight of the magnets concentrated near the centre it all adds up to making the needle dead beat – that is, straying little from the magnetic meridian in turns and changes of speed. Actually, it's not a 100% success, but at least the errors are controllable. There are sundry refinements, such as part of the bowl being made of thin corrugated metal to allow for changes in the volume of the liquid with changes in temperature – a bubble in the liquid would rather cocque things up. The liquid has the disadvantage of turning with the aircraft in a prolonged turn, taking the magnet system with it. Despite the liquid's low viscosity and the fact that the damping wires are kept short, liquid swirl does prevent an immediate settling down on a new compass Heading.

FIG 8.11

The split sleeve overlaps the ledge round the dome to prevent the whole works falling apart when flying inverted.

You are doubtless already well acquainted with the instrument and how to use it, but next time you climb aboard, take a long look at the various bits, without taking it apart, that is. Most schools and clubs have a demo model – the 'P' type has been in use for so long that there are as many u/s models around as serviceable. The only change in recent years is that the later models are built of plastic, and corrosion from the liquid is nil. The lubber line on the bowl must be fixed precisely in the fore and aft line of the aircraft. The North point on the grid is marked with a red triangle, and parallel lines are drawn across the plate to be lined up with the needle; the needle has its North seeking end crossed: the desired Heading is set at the lubber line, the ring locked, and the aircraft turned until 'red is on red'. Direction is marked every 10°, graduated in 2° divisions, luminous.

8. The E-type compass
This is a vertical-reading magnetic compass which is usually fitted by the windscreen. The bowl is of transparent plastic and the lubber line simply a luminous line in the window. The magnet is a domed steel circle and from the dome a pivot is dropped which rests in a sapphire cup on a stem fixed to the base of the bowl (Fig 8.12) Thus dip is minimised as in the P-type compass.

FIG 8.12

The bowl is filled with a silicone fluid, non-corrosive, of low viscosity and with a low coefficient of expansion – but there is a sylphon tube at the rear of the compass bowl. The compass card is a light metal ring, marked every 30°, graduated in 5° or 10°, attached to the circular magnet while the dome of the bowl prevents the system falling off when inverted. The E2 suffers from turning and acceleration errors and could in extreme climb or dive positions not be free to rotate.

9. Effect of metal objects near the compass
All ferrous metals are ready to become magnets, for it is just a matter of lining up the molecules in the same direction to give them their maximum magnetic strength. In any piece of susceptible metal there will be some magnetic influence by its very existence in the Earth's field. It follows that any metallic substance, unless it is utterly non-ferrous like brass, could affect the compass needle if brought near it, making a nonsense of the deviation card. And since we can hardly be expected to know the constituents of alloys we must be fearful of their magnetic effects as a precaution.

A magnet must have a North and South pole. If one magnet is brought near another, like poles repel each other, unlike poles attract. The North pole of a magnet brought near to the compass in the horizontal plane amidships of the bowl will repel the North pole of the compass and attract its South pole. A South pole placed end on to the North pole of the compass will tend to hold the needle there, increasing the needle's directive force. And a ferrous metal simply nearing the compass needle will have a deviating influence, even if the metal is not actually classified as a magnet; its presence is a liability in the magnet field around the needle, upsetting previous measurements and calculations in an haphazard manner.

The moral of this story is clear: if the compass is at seat level, make sure the young person in the right-hand seat hasn't got an iron bar in his trouser pocket, or a metal padlock on her chastity belt. Make sure.

10. Turning and acceleration errors

The displacement of the centre of gravity in the pendulous magnet system to counteract Dip has one or two unhappy results – except for examiners who find them a godsend. We can say that in the Northern hemisphere where the North seeking end of the needle wants to point into the Earth's surface, the centre of gravity is South of the pivot; in the Southern Hemisphere, the centre of gravity is North of the pivot to counterbalance the South seeking pole from its inclination to the middle of the globe. All this causes errors to the directional needle in turns, accelerations and decelerations, except of course at the Magnetic Equator where Z is nil.

(a) Acceleration errors

In Fig. 8.13, there is a simplified representation of the compass needle in the Northern hemisphere, showing the pivot point and the centre of gravity. The aircraft carrying the compass is on a Westerly Heading, and accelerates (Fig. 8.14).

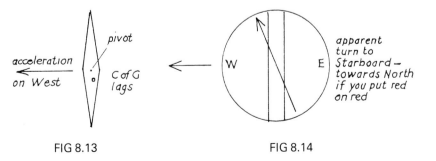

FIG 8.13   FIG 8.14

The whole works moves forward, but an equal and opposite force acts on the centre of gravity, causing the North seeking end of the needle to move in a Westerly (anti-clockwise) direction. Additionally, this lagging will give some vertical tilt to the needle, as the needle, pivot and centre of gravity are no longer in line with the magnetic meridian, so some Dip will ensue, giving Z a chance to move the North seeking end of the needle still further in the direction of acceleration.

On Easterly Headings, an acceleration would turn the needle point in a clockwise direction, as though a turn had been made to port.

In decelerations, the centre of gravity will tend to continue on its way while the rest of the mass drags back, having in each case an apparent turn effect in the opposite sense to those stated for speed increases.

When changing speeds on **Headings across the needle** there will be a compass error until constant speed is resumed. These errors can be summarised, and it's wise to check each one by a rough sketch, putting in the displaced centre of gravity.

Summary of acceleration and deceleration errors

Hdg	Speed	Needle turns	Effect
E	Increase	clockwise	Apparent turn to N
W	Increase	anticlockwise	Apparent turn to N
E	Decrease	anticlockwise	Apparent turn to S
W	Decrease	clockwise	Apparent turn to S

Note the following especially:
1. In the Southern hemisphere, the above errors are opposite.
2. There are no errors on Northerly and Southerly headings as the force acts along the needle.
3. Errors can occur in bumpy conditions.
4. No errors on the Magnetic Equator and thereabouts as the pivot and centre of gravity are coincident.

(b) *Turning errors*

These are maximum on Northerly and Southerly Headings, and are important within 35° or so of these Headings. In a turn through North to starboard the centrifugal force acts on the centre of gravity, which is displaced in our hemisphere south of the pivot. As a result, the needle turns in the direction of the turn, Easterly; and this result will be accentuated by the imbalance of centripetal force (on the pivot) and centrifugal force (on the centre of gravity) exerting a vertical pull on the slightly tilted North-seeking end of the needle, now off the magentic meridian, increasing the movement of the needle in the direction of turn.

The amount of the error depends on the rate of turn. In turns through North the needle usually shows a smaller turn than actually accomplished. You can amuse yourself by conjuring up rates of turn which result in the needle moving in such a way as to indicate no turn at all, or a turn in the wrong direction.

Through South, the compass needle will turn in the opposite direction to the aircraft, indicating a greater turn that that actually made.

The errors can be quite considerable in prolonged turns. Liquid swirl, which moves in the same direction as the turning aircraft, increases the errors through North, but is subtractive through South. In the Southern hemisphere, of course, all the conclusions mentioned will be reversed, for the centre of gravity is displaced to the North of the pivot.

All these dynamic errors last only for the period of turn or change of speed. When constant speed or straight and level flight is resumed the needle finds North again, but if you didn't know what to expect, getting on a new Heading would be a rare old fiddle.

To summarise turning errors

Direction of aircraft's turn	Direction of needle's turn	Effect	Liquid swirl	Correction
Through **North** on to East or West	Same as aircraft's turn	Under-indication	Adds to error	Turn less than needle shows
Through **South** on to East or West	Opposite to aircraft's turn	Over-indication	Reduces error	Turn more than needle shows

1. In the Southern hemisphere these errors are of opposite value.
2. In turns about East or West there are no errors to speak of because forces act along the needle.
3. Northerly turning error is greater than Southerly since liquid swirl is additive.
4. So if you have a gyro-controlled D.I. (directional indicator) use that for accurate turns.

The diagrams Figs 8.15 and 8.16, overleaf, have proved useful, but you should do a few of your own. Jot the cardinal points on a grid ring, and at the end of a turn, put red on red, and so prove to yourself visually whether the compass over- or under-reads at that stage.

It is unlikely that an exam for the PPL would be set without a question or two on compasses; usually, they are of the type to check your understanding of the matter rather than a deep knowledge. As the practical element is overriding, at least one question on compass errors is almost certain. A few samples follow:

1. In which of the following circumstances will the direct reading compass show a turn in the correct direction, but of too great an amount?
   (a) Turning from South-east to South-west in the Northern hemisphere.
   (b) Turning from South-east to South-west in the Southern hemisphere.
   (c) Turning from North-west to North-east in the Northern hemisphere.

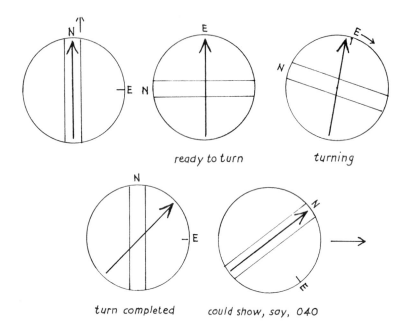

ready to turn   turning

turn completed   could show, say, 040

FIG 8.15

2. When turning in flight over the UK, on a southerly Heading the magnetic compass will:
   (a) indicate more turn than is actually made.
   (b) indicate less turn than actually made.
   (c) indicate the turn correctly.

3. When flying straight and level over the UK, the magnetic compass will indicate a turn to the left if speed is decreased when Heading:
   (a) Northerly.
   (b) Westerly.
   (c) Easterly.

4. At the Magnetic Equator:
   (a) compass deviation is nil.
   (b) Variation is nil.
   (c) Dip is nil.

5. Which of the following statements is correct?
   (a) Annual changes on the chart apply to deviation.
   (b) Deviation is the angle between the True North Pole and the Magnetic North Pole.
   (c) The deviation of a compass can change on a long flight.

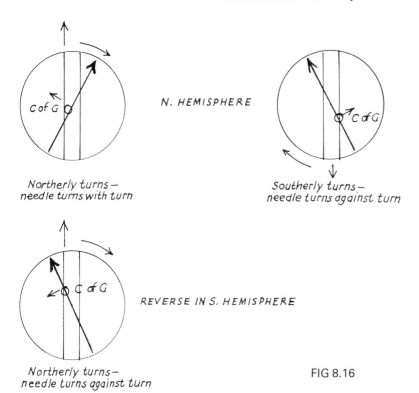

N. HEMISPHERE

Northerly turns –
needle turns with turn

Southerly turns –
needle turns against turn

REVERSE IN S. HEMISPHERE

Northerly turns –
needle turns against turn

FIG 8.16

6. A brass door knocker placed near the compass of an aircraft would affect:
   (a) the Variation.
   (b) the Deviation.
   (c) neither the Variation nor the Deviation.

7. Above 70° North latitude, the compass is useless because:
   (a) Variation is too large.
   (b) the needle will not stay horizontal.
   (c) the liquid expands.

Answers
1. a   2. a   3. b   4. c   5. c   6. c   7. b

9: Meteorology

We've no intention of getting academic here. The PPL calls for a general understanding of what causes what weather, the danger signs in weather conditions, and how to get weather reports and forecasts. In other words, you are expected to have more than enough knowledge of the topic for safe and sensible private flying.

Pressure

The air presses on the surface of the Earth, and the weight of it at any particular part depends on a number of factors – the terrain, time of day, season of the year, temperature, moisture content, among others – in that area itself and its surroundings. This gaseous envelope, the atmosphere, extends some hundreds of miles up, thin though it certainly is at such great altitudes. And of course, pressure is constantly trying to equalise itself and to flow from high pressure to low: this attempt, and it's a simplification, is wind.

Over the vast areas of land and ocean, pressures build up or decrease and move across the sphere until temperature, terrain or other pressure systems alter their values. These systems of Low and High pressure, covering from a few to thousands of square miles, are the bases of weather conditions: each system has a centre, and the pressure varies as distance from the centre varies. In the UK, pressure is measured in millibars (mb), and the derivation of the unit is scarcely our concern right now; for once, we won't even tell you all about it on the plea of interest, because it's deadly dull. You will, perhaps, as you fly around the world come up against a State where pressure is measured in inches of mercury. 1 000 mb = 29·53 in, but there is no convenient aide-memoire, only plenty of conversion tables to shove in your flight bag on a trip abroad. Many overseas countries know the unit which in the UK we call a millibar as a hectopascal. The barometer is the instrument used to measure pressure. At mean sea level in the UK, pressure usually varies from about 970 mb to 1 030 mb over the year, and whenever a Met station measures the pressure it must be reduced to sea level before transmission to the Met Office where it will be plotted on a chart.

Keep thinking of pressure as the weight of a column of air. If you climb to 5 000 ft, then there is 5 000 ft beneath you, and that amount less pressing on your aircraft. The International Standard Atmosphere (ISA) takes pressure as 1013·2 mb at mean sea level, and the decrease of pressure with height is of the rough order of 1 mb per 30 ft. The altimeter is an aneroid barometer (meaning no liquid in it) which indicates the pressure on a dial marked out in feet of altitude.

Synoptic charts

You are already familiar with some type of these charts from TV and newspapers. If we confine ourselves to pressure for the moment, the pressures at mean sea level are plotted for a large number of stations. The met man then draws in the lines of equal pressure, called isobars, every 2 mb or more depending on the size of the area he's coping with. A pattern of Highs and Lows emerges on the chart from which he can deduce and forecast the weather for the period in any part of the area covered, in the air or on the ground. The charts are drawn up for 3 or 6 hourly periods, as the importance of the station warrants, always at 0000 hr and on.

Pressure systems and their weather

Before belting out the three types for each of High and Low, we must refer to a couple of terms frequently used about wind direction, and frequently muddled. When the wind **backs**, its change of direction is anticlockwise, e.g. a wind of 250/40 will back to become 230/40. You can think of it as getting a lower figure in the 360° circuit, though a wind of 020/30 would back to become 350/30.

When the wind **veers**, its change of direction is clockwise, e.g. a wind of 190/30 will veer to become 210/30; it has veered 20°.

The free air wind is taken to be at around 2 000 ft, where it is assumed to be away from the frictional effects of the Earth's surface. A wind of, say, 240/40 at 2 000 ft may become 220/25 at ground level; it has backed and reduced in speed because of the drag of the surface terrain – in this case, a roughish terrain. A free air wind might not back quite as much as that over a calm sea, nor lose 15 kt of speed; possibly, it would be 230/30 at sea level in quiet conditions. Run through that lot again, it will make the ensuing material even clearer.

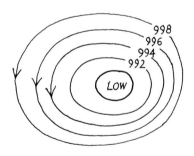

FIG 9.1 A Low or Depression

In a depression, the isobars, given a value above in Fig. 9.1 for illustration, are usually evenly spaced and closed. A depression is referred to as 'intense' or 'shallow'. The free air wind blows around the isobars in an anti-clockwise direction in the Northern hemisphere, whereas at the surface, friction backs the wind towards the centre of the Low. **Buys Ballot's Law** states that if you stand with your back to the wind in the Northern hemisphere, the lower pressure is on your left hand side.

The tighter the isobars, the more intense the depression and the faster the wind speed; the pressure is changing fast in other words, and the weather can be violent. A tornado is nothing but an intense depression, covering perhaps a few hundred yards; a shallow depression can spread over thousands of miles, giving relatively gentle winds and light weather. Air is always flowing into a Low at the surface because the pressure there is less however vast the area the depression covers. The inflowing air rises, eventually 'filling up' the depression; and rising air will cool. If this cooling air is moist enough, then the basic conditions exist for cloud formation and precipitation (rain, snow, hail, and so on).

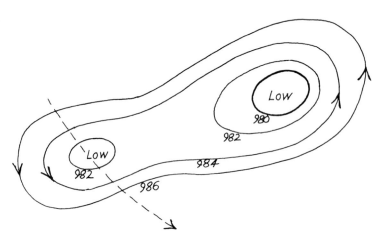

FIG 9.2 Secondary Depresion

A separate centre of low pressure can develop (Fig. 9.2) within the primary low and may be caused by an unbalanced inflow of air from surrounding Highs, by unequal rising of air within the parent Low due to varying terrain, or simply cold air warming in part of the area. These secondaries tend to rotate anticlockwise round the parent. Winds in the secondaries obey Buys Ballot's law but are usually stronger than in the primary Low and the precipitation heavier; gales can develop on the side away from the main Low especially in winter.

In a Trough, the isobars take on the shape illustrated (Fig. 9.3) with the wind veering sharply as the trough line passes. The movement of the Trough is at right angles to the 'trough line' and the weather is much as for a shallow depression, improving rapidly after the passage of the trough line.

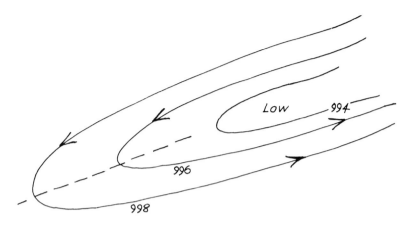

FIG 9.3 Trough of Low Pressure

The isobars in a High are closed but not regular in shape, and fairly wide apart (Fig. 9.4). The air is heavy, pressing down on the surface, as it were, trying to diverge towards the lower pressures. Hence, it is an area of subsiding air, inhibiting cloud formation. Winds are light, with a large area of central calm. In the free air, the wind blows in a clockwise direction around the isobars in the Northern hemisphere, while at the surface the associated frictional backing takes the flow away from the centre.

The weather, with little cloud, can be said to be quiet and stable rather than always good. There is no precipitation, but the subsiding air and light winds prevent the dispersal of fog, industrial haze and smoke, and because

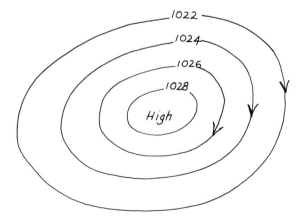

FIG 9.4 High or Anticylone

a High can be stationary over a big area (it moves slowly and erratically at best) the smog can persist for days. Clear skies at night and light winds can cause radiation fog at any time, given the required moisture conditions – the humidity in the UK is usually just right. Fog of this type is discussed later. Another likely result of nocturnal radiation is cooling air near the ground, and if the air a few thousand feet up maintains its approximate day time temperature, then an inversion of temperature will occur. With an inversion the norm of a decrease of temperature with height is halted for a layer, but then resumes above it. Beneath the inversion, blanket cloud can form, which in summer is readily dispelled after sun-up, but in winter can persist.

A ridge (Fig. 9.5) is an extension of a High in one direction, and is relatively fast moving, often in a North-easterly direction over the UK. The weather is fair or fine with no cloud and light winds, but the speed of its movement means that it isn't long before the influence of an associated depression is felt.

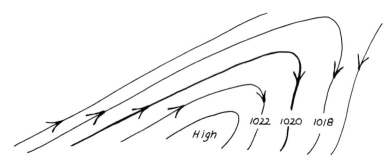

FIG 9.5 Ridge of High Pressure

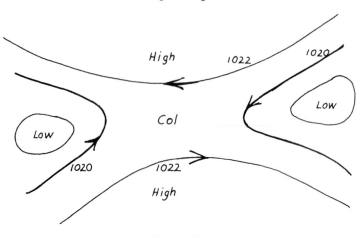

FIG 9.6 Col

A col (Fig. 9.6) is a region of uniform pressure separating two Highs and two Lows. From what has been said about gently subsiding air in a High and gently rising air in a Low, it will be seen that in a col there is a diversity of inflow and outflow. Winds are light to calm, variable in direction if measurable at all, which is unlikely. Such conditions can lead to fog, low cloud in winter, thunderstorms in summer with heating of land surfaces. A col is not a dominant factor in the synoptic situation by the very nature of the conditions which make it up – the effect of the neighbouring Highs and Lows must erode it in due course.

Fronts

The frequent changeability of weather in the temperate zones between Tropics and Poles is basically caused by the meeting of warm and cold air. The warm air rises over the colder, and the pressure drops forming a depression. In that depression, then, we have two distinct airflows, one the original cold, the other the intruding warm; and there is nothing stationary about a depression either.

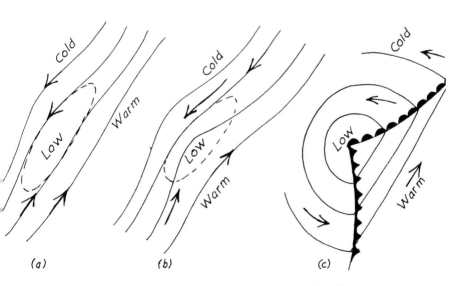

FIG 9.7 Formation of a Low, with Warm and Cold Fronts.

The area of warm or tropical air is called the warm sector, that of cold or polar air, the cold sector. Where the warm air is overtaking the cold air is the warm front so the other front where cold air is advancing is the cold front.

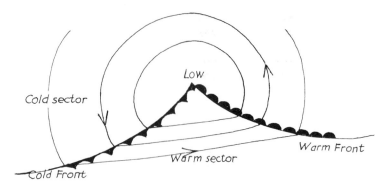

FIG 9.8

On a synoptic chart, a warm front is coloured red, a cold front blue. Where only a single colour is used the fronts are symbolised as in Fig. 9.8, and the symbols referred to, even by the pure in heart, as warm tits and cold tits.

There is a definite weather pattern associated with the passage of fronts, though the intensity of weather will depend on the temperature difference between before and after the front, the season of the year, the surface over which the front has passed, and the origins of the air masses which we have mentioned above, broadly, as 'polar' and 'tropical'. Fig. 9.9 illustrates a typical frontal system, a picture that should be kept in mind at pre-flight met briefings, for the ingredients are there for poor visibility, turbulence, and icing. Make a note of the average distances involved.

A cold front moves rather faster than a warm one. In Fig 9.9 the slope of the cold front and its horizontal coverage indicate this. Eventually, the cold front will catch up the warm, and start 'occluding', or shutting off the warm air from the ground. Occlusion weather will be a mixture of the two fronts, not lasting long and not so intense at the surface. The symbol on the chart is cold and warm tits alternating (Fig. 9.10, page 114).

The recognition of warm and cold fronts will be clear from the diagrams: the cloud formations, the associated precipitation, the marked veer in wind at the passage, the change in temperature. In flight, after a well-understood met briefing and with the issued chart open in the cockpit, the approach of a front can be spotted or felt, and any precautions taken to avoid dangerous or uncomfortable conditions – and if the front clamps your destination, divert to another field.

Winds

Fundamentally, the air tries to move from high pressure to low pressure, and we have already noted that there is subsiding air in a High and some

FIG 9.9 Warm and Cold Front Systems

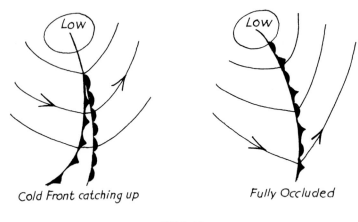

Cold Front catching up   Fully Occluded

FIG 9.10

resultant divergence to the Low. In consequence, a Low has air converging on it and rising within it. If that were all, the flow from High to Low would end in equation. It doesn't, and the reason why is highly technical. Fortunately, for the needs of the PPL examination, we can be content with the statement of fact.

The Earth's rotation causes the wind to bear to the right in the Northern hemisphere, to the left in the Southern. Consult the pressure system diagrams and check what's happened, as well as the truth of Buys Ballot's Law. This turning force is called the **geostrophic force**, and the free air wind is called the **geostrophic wind** – well, more often than not, anyway. Anything moving on a small circle path has centrifugal elements, called the **cyclostrophic force**, and this would be noticeable in a Low. The combination of the two forces produces the **gradient wind**. But the geostrophic component may in general terms be considered overriding, since it is always present, while the cyclostrophic presupposes some sort of circular motion.

On a synoptic chart, the geostrophic wind – and we stress the fact we're talking about the free air – can be measured in direction with a protractor as usual, and in speed by the distance between the isobars read against a special scale in the corner of the chart. Thus, the chart, though made up of sea level observations, maps the airflow unimpeded by surface friction; surface drag to some extent breaks down the geostrophic flow by backing it.

The wind even in the free air does not blow steadily in strength or direction, for there are always variations in temperatures, densities and humidities, vertically and on the level. A **gale** (defined as a wind of at least 34 kt lasting 10 minutes or more) can happen anywhere in the firmament; but a **squall** (the wind increasing suddenly by 16 kt or more to become at least 22 kt for one minute or longer) demands met conditions such as exist at a lively cold front. Near the ground, the antics of the wind, whatever its basic strength from the pressure situation, are determined by the topography, and very nasty these antics can be at times for the pilot.

In **gusts and lulls**, short lived sudden increases and drops in wind speed near the surface, unequal heating and vertical wind shear have their place, but obstructions are a most important factor. Wind striking a hangar, say, is thrust up, flows roughly and irregularly over and around the building, a lull forms in the lee, with a biggish gust on the reunion of the eddies beyond. The effect over hills, cliffs, and such, is similar. The down wind side is the danger side, for eddies will have developed on the leeward which themselves travel downwards, producing dramatic gusts and lulls in high wind conditions. It follows that the higher the obstruction, the greater the danger to leeward. It's worth mentioning that friction will fluctuate the wind over any undulating ground and there are airfields aplenty on land which is far from prairie-like. Even over dead flat ground, drag produces eddies and minor turbulence which in theory should be absent.

A **valley wind** is easily understood; the wind blowing against a range of hills is impeded, and if a gap breaks the barrier, the speed up that valley is greatly increased by the suction effect, if that's a way of putting it. The direction of the original flow is a determining factor in the strength of a valley wind, as it won't happen if the flow is at right angles to the general direction of the valley.

Land and sea breezes are best explained with the following picture (Fig. 9.11).

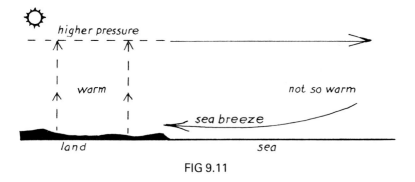

FIG 9.11

We're on the coast early after noon on a warm summer's day; the land heats up whereas the sea hardly changes. The warm air expands, and the pressure a few hundred feet above the land surface will become greater than at the same height over the sea, a bit of a vertical artificial pile-up, at height, of air; thus, a flow begins at height, from overland to oversea. The air near the surface of the coast is depleted, pressure there falls; for the similar column over the sea, the pressure remains comparatively high. As a result there is a flow near the surface from sea to land, a **Sea Breeze**. Sea breezes can be quite squally and sudden, and some care should be taken when landing in the afternoon at coastal aerodromes. At night, the reverse happens; the land cools quickly, the sea doesn't, and the flow is from land to sea at the surface – a **Land Breeze**. Never tell a Met man, examiner or not, that a Sea Breeze is caused by hot air rising, so air comes from the sea to take its place; that will never do, and will make his bottle-green pullover ride up even further at the waist.

A rider here is the effect on landing conditions during a warm day of turbulence caused by convection currents; convection is just hot air expanding and rising, but it can be violent. An approach to land at midday over water, which has nil convection, can become rough as the aircraft passes over scorched fields or concrete areas at the coast, and this at a time when the aircraft is low and speeds are well reduced.

Standing Waves have had great prominence in recent years, as they have indeed been the cause of some nasty accidents. When air flows over hills or mountains, air over and to the leeward side may be disturbed to great heights and for many miles downwind (FIg. 9.12). The hills induce a wave-like form to the wind flow above and to the lee, with a rotor turbulence in the lower levels. The waves are **stationary**, hence the name. The conditions most favourable for the formation of standing waves are a constant wind direction and a stable layer of air above the mountain crest, i.e., little or no temperature change for a few thousand feet.

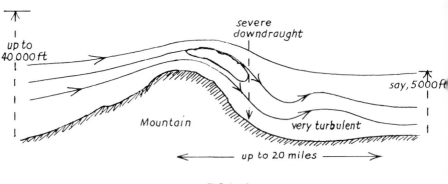

FIG 9.12

Recognition in flight is reduced to an occasional lens-shaped (lenticular) cloud, and often not even that. The vertical movement is considerable and on the downwind side really dangerous. If standing waves are forecast or known to exist, avoid such areas entirely if possible. If you must fly near, allow the maximum safety margin, like clearing the hills by twice their height amsl – for a hill of 2 000 ft, fly at 6 000 ft, and you might get away with just severe turbulence. Standing waves will break up with a change in the pressure pattern for it's the steady wind in a stable atmosphere which is ideal for their build-up.

Lapse Rate

Temperature decreases with height but the rate of change, or lapse rate, is scarcely ever in line with the accepted standard of 1·98°C per 1 000 ft. The very fact that the Earth absorbs the heat radiated (i.e. by electromagnetic waves) from the Sun, warms the air at ground level (conduction), which then rises (convection), gives a clue to the folly of assuming the average, especially as all that's without mention of sand, forest, concrete, hills, mountains, and what all.

Warm air rises, and if it expands, the work done is expressed in terms of heat loss; the temperature falls, but there is no transference of heat – it is still there, within the expanded volume of air. Such changes in the condition of a parcel of air, which take place without heat transfer, are called 'adiabatic'. Unsaturated air is air which contains its moisture content invisibly, before it reaches a temperature low enough to 'condense' its vapour into visible droplets. That temperature is called the 'dew point'. We're certainly piling on the definitions here. And unsaturated air rising, however caused, loses temperature at a constant and certain rate of 3°C per 1 000 ft (there's a strong move afoot to force us all to say it's 1°C per 100 metres, so help me). This is the Dry Adiabatic Lapse Rate (DALR). When the parcel is high enough and cold enough to condense the excess invisible vapour, latent heat is given out in the process, reducing the lapse rate by about half. The Saturated Adiabatic Lapse Rate (SALR) is taken to be 1·5°C per 1 000 ft, though this is a mean, for it varies. The DALR and SALR are lapse rates for rising air, remember.

FIG 9.13 Stability

Now a mass of air, caused to rise by some external force, which then returns of its own accord is 'stable': when the DALR is more than the lapse rate of its surrounding environment, the mass will fall back. The Environmental Lapse Rate (ELR) is just whatever is the lapse rate round the parcel in question (see Fig. 9.13, page 117).

In the converse case with an ELR the same as or greater than the DALR, the mass will continue to rise apparently without limit while these conditions last. This is 'instability', (Fig. 9.14).

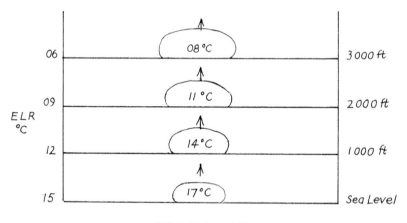

FIG 9.14 Instability

The main reason for this brief sortie into the purlieus of physics is to introduce the language in the following paragraphs about clouds, which must have a niche, even if we only consider their part in the stark requirement of the PPL syllabus which says 'Flying conditions to avoid'.

Clouds

We are breaking with a hoary tradition by excluding photos of cloud types which, in fact, take numerous forms. Your flying instructor in making you weather-conscious, will point out the types prevailing each time you fly. Your club or local reference library will probably hold one of the many books devoted entirely to cloud photographs.

There are two groups of cloud: stratiform, or layer cloud, and cumuliform, or heap cloud. Stratiform is quiet, mainly the result of stable air with a decrease of temperature with height. Cumuliform implies rising air and it is within this broad group that the dangerous types are found, with some reservations, of course. We split the types into high, medium and low for convenience, but there is often a merging of the types, with obvious implications to the pilot.

High, from about 20 000 ft and up but lower in winter and in high latitudes.

Cirrus (Ci), wispy, made up of ice crystals, of no significance in flying, nil precipitation since all the vapour's virtually gone at that height and temperature.

Cirro-stratus (Cs), veil type cloud, which gives a halo to the Moon; of no significance.

Cirro-cumulus (Cc), the well-known globular, white, mackerel sky; again, of no flying significance.

Medium, from about 6 000 ft to 23 000 ft.

Altocumulus (Ac), larger cloudlets, denser, visibility within is poor; little or no precipitation; moderate turbulence; light icing.

Altostratus (As), sheet cloud often of considerable vertical thickness; visibility can be poor, but otherwise of little flying significance except over high ground where it may give airframe icing problems.

Low, from as low as the ground to about 7 000 ft.

Nimbostratus (Ns), thick dark grey cloud, full of water, 'nimbus' is the Latin for rain, so they say; flying is smooth, visibility is not there at all, precipitation can be heavy, and so can icing.

Stratus (St), thin sheet cloud, white; poor visibility, no other significance except it can cover the tops of hills.

Stratocumulus (Sc), thin, lumpy cloud; poor visibility, some bumpiness, otherwise of small significance.

Of special importance, from as low as ground level to massive heights.

Cumulus (Cu), isolated, of considerable vertical development, white; poor visibility, bumpy indeed, and icing to a dangerous degree. Domed top, heavy showers.

Cumulonimbus (Cb), black, great vertical development, anvil top, often isolated. It has the lot, dangerous turbulence, dangerous icing, heavy rain, hail, and thunderstorms to boot. Avoid like the plague.

The term 'lenticular' is given to a lens shaped cloud such as was mentioned in the Standing waves topic: the prefix 'fracto' refers to broken cloud.

This is a good spot to define the various sorts or precipitation:

Drizzle is the fall of minute water droplets, imperceptible on the surface of your swimming pool.

Rain is the fall of bigger water droplets making distinct splashes.

Snow is the coalescence of ice crystals which become too heavy to be held suspended. If the air below the cloud is cold enough they reach the ground as snow; if not, they fall as rain. You can be flying in snow, but the ground is in rain.

Sleet: rain and snow together – temperature around the melting point.

Hail: small ice chunks, rounded by friction. The clatter on the fuselage is the worst effect unless they're very large. Tropical hailstones from marble-size to golfball size can do structural damage.

Continuity: Given as continuous, intermittent or showers. The first is self-evident; the difference between the latter is depicted in figure 9.15, intermittent precipitation falling from time to time usually from a generally overcast sky while showers fall from the individual cumuliform clouds with which they are associated. Hence you never get showers of drizzle.

Overcast with intermittent precipitation   Showers and bright intervals

FIG 9.15

Visibility

This is the maximum horizontal distance at which objects can be easily recognised by the naked eye. It is usually reported in kilometres and metres. There's little need to elaborate on the weather that causes poor visibility – it can be dust, smoke or any old rubbish in the air, it can be visible moisture from fog, through drizzle to pouring rain and snow. There are one or two accepted definitions which a pilot must know.

Fog is when visibility is reduced to less than 1 km (1 100 yards) due to water droplets and/or smoke or dust particles.

Mist is when reduced visibility, due entirely to water droplets, is more than 1 km.

Haze is visibility reduced because of dust particles and such in the atmosphere, with no upper or lower limits to the horizontal visibility.

The visibility by night is largely dependent on the strength of the observed lights and the optical rating of the observer's eye. The met observers have evolved a method of rationalising this, and night vis reports have always proved satisfactory. Enough said.

Before pressing on to a discussion on fog, beware when viewing an aerodrome which is in a shallow layer of fog from vertically above it; when you turn on to final approach, the **slant** visibility may be absurdly poor (Fig. 9.16).

And by day, looking down sun improves your visibility, no dazzle, whereas by night, you can see better up moon.

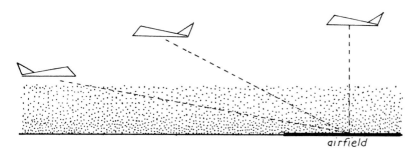

Fig 9.16

Radiation Fog is frequent and is a night-time build up. With clear skies at night, the Earth loses its heat by radiation to the surrounding air. If there's a good breeze blowing, the cold air at the surface will be taken up and cloud will form. If there's no wind at all, dew or frost will form. If there's a **light** wind of 3 to 8 kt, certainly less than 10 kt, sufficient movement is present to stir up the layers in direct contact with the cooling Earth, and take it away from the surface to give fog. Radiation won't take place if the sky is obscured by cloud, for this acts as an insulating blanket. Of course, a pre-requisite is moist air, or as we say, the relative humidity must be high (relative humidity is the amount of moisture the air holds expressed as a percentage of the maximum it could hold) and in the UK, the relative humidity is seldom less than 60%, and is often much more. Another essential requirement for radiation fog is that the temperature of the air must be near to the dew point. Thus, getting a weather report for the late evening of nil cloud, W/V 230/05, temperature 4°C, dew point 2°C, the area is all lined up for radiation fog to form very soon after the fall of darkness, and it will continue to form by radiation from the top of the layer, thickening in vertical extent. The longer the night, the thicker and denser the fog, so it can readily become a clampus magnus in winter which only a wind can disperse. In summer, radiation fog is prevalent around dawn, and not being of much depth, the stronger summer sunshine quickly clears the fog.

Over hills, the denser air near the ground tends to roll down to the bottom, having the effect of thickening the fog in the valley and low lying areas. This draining is called the 'katabatic' effect – we thought you'd like to know. There are plenty of airfields which get the works in that manner, though.

Advection Fog, the other type to mention, is movement fog: simply the passage of air over a surface where the temperature is below the air's dew point. The air must have a high relative humidity. An example is warm air travelling over cooler sea in Spring or early summer round the British Isles when the sea still holds on to its winter temperature. The resulting fog can be dragged well inland but its persistence, and indeed its occurrence, are not seriously comparable to the radiation type.

Runway Visual Range (RVR). As fog is a governing condition in landing, a system has been devised of reporting the actual visibility along the runway at 15 ft above the centre line, when it's below 1 100 metres. There's no forecasting about this, it's a factual report from half-hourly (or more if conditions are changeable) observations at many civil airfields. The responsibility for the job is with Traffic Control, not with the Met Office. The RVR is included in broadcasts for many aerodromes in active civil use, but is given to aircraft 15 minutes before ETA for nearly any field where landing is proposed. Bear in mind that fog is not uniformly dense; it does swirl, and the RVR can alter between the time of observation and the time of receipt by the pilot.

Icing

It's all dangerous, or indicative of coming danger. An aircraft left out on a calm clear night in dead of winter will be covered in **hoar frost** quite quickly. A take-off, with the temperature still below freezing and the frost still on, will need a longer run to unstick and the stalling speed will be increased, for the rough surface on the fabric has ruined the airflow over the wings. In fact, hoar frost may prevent the aircraft getting airborne at all. Hoar frost can occur in clear air (the emphasis is on clear air) when descending with a cold aircraft into warmer, moister conditions. The moisture in the vicinity of the aeroplane condenses as ice crystals onto the fabric, whose temperature is below freezing and below the dew point of the surrounding air. Missing out the liquid stage in the condensation from vapour to visible ice is known as 'sublimation'. That's enough, for it won't last long, but vision will be obscured, and the radio might play up for a while.

Icing in flight is invariably caused by the presence of water droplets in below freezing conditions. Droplets taken up into the atmosphere where the temperature is sub-zero Celsius (formerly Centrigrade) continue to exist in a liquid state, a state said to be 'supercooled'. Given half a chance or less, these droplets will turn into ice – and striking an aircraft is just what's required. The droplet doesn't freeze entirely on contact: 1/80 freezes for every degree of supercooling (a fancy way of saying for every degree the temperature is below 0°C). If the temperature is −5°C, then 5/80 will freeze on striking, and the other 75/80 flows back over the upper surfaces of the aeroplane, freezing on contact. All this is **clear ice**, and the more the water, and the nearer the temperature is to 0°C, the more severe the icing. It forms on the leading edges, and on all projections like propellers and pressure heads, it's hard and sticks tight. The freezing flowback alters the aerodynamic properties of the aircraft whose weight increases. After some build-up, shape on leading edges is lost and jagged protrusions appear; these break off in the most irregular lumps and cause some nasty vibrations. Clear ice is mostly found in cloud of high water content, Cb, Cu and Ns.

At lower temperatures (−40°C is about the lowest temperature for super-cooled water droplets to exist), there's not so much water; the droplets are very small, so small that they will really freeze on impact. The **rime ice** forms on all leading edges, but this time there is no flow back; the rime is white, opaque, and air is trapped between the frozen drops in a honeycomb effect. It is light, breaks off easily, and again its size and shape makes the aeroplane not the one you knew in its flying characteristics. Rime forms in the tops of Cu, and must be watched for in As, Ac, St and Sc.

A mixture of clear ice and rime ice is very possible of course, and the faster you move through any ice-forming conditions, and the longer you're in such cloud, the more intense the icing.

Flying in air below 0°C with rain falling from a warmer layer above (check the vertical cross section of the fronts of Fig. 9.9), will give **rain ice** in no time at all. It's clear ice, but forms over the entire upper surfaces of the aeroplane; the danger is the sheer weight of the stuff and its rapid build-up.

Icing must always be suspected and prepared for in cloud where temperatures are below zero Celsius. The presence of large drops, such as in Cu cloud and, worse, in Cb, is obvious and ominous. Such droplets can exist in temperatures as low as −20°C. In cloud of heavy water content like Ns, temperatures near freezing are the most dangerous. In stratiform cloud, icing is seldom dangerous except where it occurs over high ground. But for icing possibility, no temperature can be laid down as a limit.

The action to be taken is to be watchful in the first place. The early warning sign is in the corners of the wind shield, then a polished or white look about the leading edge, then a drop of a few knots in the airspeed. All this in quite a short time. If in Cu cloud, which is mainly an isolated cloud anyway, retreat. In stratus type where icing is not so serious, climb if possible, for the cloud is seldom more than a few thousand feet thick, and the chance of dangerous icing diminishes at temperatures below −7°C. And if you get into rain ice, try to get into the warm air above, but watch you don't start travelling along the warm front itself. If in doubt, turn back before the problem becomes serious.

Met forecasts will always include a specific reference to rain ice if its occurrence is even slightly probable for the route. Additionally, the forecast gives an 'icing index' – low, moderate or high – as an indication of the expected **rate** of ice formation. Special attention has been given recently by met officers to the needs of light aircraft in flight by the provision of warnings of icing, moderate or high, below flight level 100. Such warnings will have been included in the met forecast before take-off, if they existed then.

Carburettors are a problem. Petrol evaporation, plus air whipping through, can cause a drop in temperature of as much as 25°C. Carb icing can happen then on a warm afternoon in summer with a goodish relative humidity of say 60%, with the engine idling and thus not giving enough heat to melt any forming ice. The use of carb heat at the moment of suspicion is advisable, but there are reservations and modifications as to **how** it is used, and this must be learned from your flying instructor.

In general, serious icing conditions often prevail, but can be avoided; as always, it's loss of vigilance that leads to danger.

Altimeter settings

These come under the heading of terms used in aviation forecasts and reports, as laid down in the syllabus. Whether they appear in exam questions for the PPL or not, they are bandied about so much and so loosely that we think it imperative to include them in our story.

A barometer reads the pressure at a place; an aneroid barometer contains no liquid; the altimeter is an aneroid barometer which reads in feet. As its functioning presupposes a drop in pressure per so many feet of altitude, there must be a starter pressure from which to do the measuring. And mean sea level pressure is constantly changing. To help solve the problem, the altimeter is fitted with a window in which a given pressure can be set by turning a small knob. This setting on the sub-scale depends on circumstances, take-off, landing, route flying, aircraft separation, and so on; each of three settings is given a Q code.

QFE, the actual pressure at an airfield. Set on the sub-scale at the end of the runway, the altimeter reads 0 feet; take off and do a circuit and the altimeter reads height above the aerodrome. It is sensible airmanship to have the QFE set for landing. It is always available on the ground or in the air, at or for any airfield.

QNE is defined as the altimeter indication on landing with the sub-scale set at 1013·2 mb. The term has come by common usage to mean just 1013·2 mb, the standard sea level pressure, but this won't do for examiners, of course. An aircraft ordered to Flight Level 10 000 ft (FL 100) would set 1013·2 on the sub-scale. In all UK control areas, and anywhere in the UK above what is called Transition Altitude, usually 3 000 ft, 1013·2 is set by everyone to ensure flight separation.

QNH. This one is a trifle tricky: it is the aerodrome pressure reduced to mean sea level by the use of the ISA formula (if you've forgotten what that is, there's a list of abbreviations at the end of the book). As the altimeter works on this formula too, at the end of the runway with QNH set the altimeter will read the exact elevation of the field. In flight, it will read altitude above sea level in that area. This setting ensures terrain clearance, especially as a minimum of 1 000 ft above any hills, obstruction, and etc., is aimed for.

'Regional QNH' takes care of changing pressure. The UK is divided into various Altimeter Setting Regions (ASR), and each region forecasts the lowest pressure value likely to prevail in that area per hour. New values are issued on change of the hour and remain valid for that region during that hour. A pilot can obtain regional QNH up to one hour ahead of the current hour if required. Remember, it is the **lowest forecast regional QNH**. A further safety margin is thus included against obstructions for aircraft on the routes. An airfield QNH and regional QNHs are always freely obtainable before and during flight. In flight, above 3 000 ft, the altimeter would be set to QNE, to prevent collisions, the other (if carried) to QNH to clear obstacles. It's all the pilot's responsibility to fly safely, of course, and when flying on QNE he must know the value of the QNH altitude.

QFF is not, repeat not, an altimeter setting but we sling it in as it is a meteorological matter and frequently confused. It is the precise pressure at mean sea level at a given place. For QFF, barometer readings at any station are reduced to sea level by a formula based on the prevailing conditions (QNH is based on ISA, note the difference), for plotting on the synoptic chart. It is a function of the met observer, and is too variable over an area for determination of aircraft height.

FIG 9.17

Fig 9.17 illustrates how an altimeter is affected by the setting: 30 ft per millibar is a reasonable average for mental calculation, and you will remark that if the sub-scale setting is turned **down**, the reading goes down.

Thunderstorms

These occur in unstable air, plenty of moisture, plenty of uplift, however caused. Cb cloud is the major sinner, but thunderstorms can occur in a fairly widish belt along a lively cold front.

In Cb, the banging together of the droplets and the up and down currents of pretty considerable vertical extent engender the electricity which produces lightning – all this, too, often in individual pockets or cells within the cloud, some of which pockets are forming, some active, some dissipating. This type of Cb is mainly in summer, with strong surface heating and little wind: wind is adverse to such a formation, as it inhibits straight convection.

Along cold fronts, the nose of the front pushes up the warm air; if the temperature differential fore and aft of the front is big, the slope of the front will be steep, and thunderstorms can form. Mainly, this is the winter type in the UK.

The greatest danger in thunderstorm flying is the severe turbulence, as you would expect, to the extent of making aircraft control difficult. Additionally, pressure instruments like the altimeter, airspeed indicator, vertical speed indicator will be highly untrustworthy, due to pressure variations in or near the storm. Icing is ever present in such conditions, helped by rain; hail might be damaging. Lightning, apart from being disconcerting, is seldom dangerous, as the aircraft takes it safely, but the magnetic compass and radio can be affected.

In general, avoid thunderstorms. The possibility is usually forecast by the Met Office. Cb cloud is isolated, and the approach of a sharp cold front is recognisable. If inadvertently caught, as turbulence and icing are the hazards, throttle back (to slow cruising), concentrate on maintaining correct attitude with the artificial horizon, never chase the altimeter or airspeed indicator. Do not descend, unless very sure of ground clearance and position, for the cloud base is low. Cockpit lighting should be kept at its brightest as a measure against the blinding flashes of lightning; the visibility will be nil, hold Heading and height as far as possible. In the cold front type, gaps often appear which give the pilot a chance to escape.

Never take off or land in thunderstorms. The surface wind changes direction and speed dramatically, so delay take-off or landing except, as they say, in cases of force majeure for a landing.

And we congratulate ourselves on saying all this without once taking a trip down memory lane.

Wind Shear
The possibility of inconsistency of winds at low level in thunderstorms has just been mentioned. Unfortunately this may also occur on other occasions with potentially hazardous consequences. If ATC warn you that a wind shear is probable, take it literally – the wind may be changing very significantly in a very small change of altitude, making a climb-out or descent path virtually impossible to hold. With a squall and a downdraught in a cloud-burst situation, conditions will be even worse for a light aircraft.

Reports and forecasts
A **report** is a statement of weather conditions that exist or existed at a particular time and place. A **forecast** is a statement of weather conditions

which are expected at a particular time and place. A pilot seeking information must be explicit about whether he wants a report or a forecast. When planning a trip, a pilot should warn the Met Office which covers his aerodrome of his requirements, at least 2 hours prior for a flight up to 500 miles, and 4 hours prior for longer flights. The Met Office will want his intended route, the period of the flight, the proposed flight level, and the time the forecast is to be collected.

Any one of the above statements is a stone bonker for the PPL examination.

Small airfields do not have Met Offices on the spot, but the needs of pilots anywhere in the country are filled by a nearby main or subsidiary Met Office by phone. This is not done by some dreary clerk, but by a qualified officer, who will not only give the briefing and forecast as required, but will answer any questions about the route and aerodrome weather the pilot asks. And it's notable that every Met Office has the full facilities of a main Met Office immediately available, and that information is just about limitless. Before flight, too, much use is made of met broadcasts, continuous or non-continuous, from central Control Centres like London, Scotland, Preston, which give **reports** of weather conditions at selected aerodromes in plain language for specific times. 'Trend' is often added to these reports, a forecast of visibility, low cloud amount and base for the subsequent 2 hours of the stated time.

A flight forecast contains:

The period of validity; if departure is delayed beyond it, a new forecast must be requested.

A statement for the route of the met situation, fronts, pressure systems and so on. The route itself will be divided as the weather merits at the points of change.

Over the route, winds and temperatures at the surface and at pressure altitudes up to the altitude requested. Winds, of course, in direction True and knots, temperatures in °C.

Cloud, low and high, type in the accepted abbreviations, amount in oktas of sky coverage (it's eighths, actually, 8/8 is completely overcast, 1/8 is scarcely any), and height of base in feet amsl.

Surface visibility.

Weather, especially precipitation.

Height of the 0° isotherm.

Any remarks about turbulence, icing index, warnings.

Then will follow forecasts for airfields, the departure and destination ones and alternates for both – period of validity, surface W/V, visibility, weather, amount, type and height of base of lowest and second layer cloud. The height of base of cloud over an airfield is the height above the field itself, whereas on the route it's given amsl within 50 nm of the departure field and as a pressure height above 1013·2 mb beyond that limit. This may seem rather complicated, but it's important in practice, as landing and take-off demand clearance over the runway itself, 50 nm is the area of climb or descent, and en route, FL is the norm.

Odd terms are flung around, occasionally self explanatory, all defined with legal precision somewhere or other. CAVOK means that there's no cloud to speak of and visibility is just about unlimited; gradu, rapid, tempo, inter(mittent), prob 40% meaning (there's a 3 to 2 chance this won't happen). Warnings in flight are 'Sigmet' – of thunderstorms, squalls, ice, fog, turbulence – significant met information in other words, often followed by diversion advice. These warnings are sent out by Control Centre or Approach Control, having emanated from Met who disseminated them to Air Traffic Control Centres; thence it's the Traffic chain of command for the area.

We conclude this section with a few questions of the sort posed hitherto, together with answers at the end.

1. Drizzle is precipitation
    (a) not lasting long
    (b) consisting of small drops
    (c) small in amount

2. You require a route forecast and met briefing for a flight of 400 nm. What is minimum period of notice to be given?
    (a) 4 hours
    (b) 2 hours
    (c) 1 hour

3. Hoar frost can form on an aircraft
    (a) in freezing rain
    (b) in stratus cloud
    (c) in clear air

4. In a depression, the free air wind blows
    (a) clockwise in the northern hemisphere
    (b) anti-clockwise in the southern hemisphere
    (c) clockwise in the southern hemisphere

5. Approaching a range of hills with a tailwind, up currents are
    (a) on the approach side of the hills
    (b) on the far side of the hills
    (c) on both sides of the hills

6. A report of weather at an airfield
    (a) forecasts landing conditions
    (b) gives the weather for time of take-off or landing
    (c) gives the weather existing at the time stated

7. CAVOK means
    (a) altimeter set to regional QNH
    (b) visibility reduced by smoke
    (c) little cloud and almost unlimited visibility

8. Turbulence is most severe in
   - (a) stratocumulus
   - (b) cumulonimbus
   - (c) altocumulus

9. In Cb cloud, severe airframe icing is most likely in temperatures of
   - (a) $-25°C$
   - (b) $-5°C$
   - (c) $-40°C$

10. Cloud base at BODGER'S Field is reported as 300 feet. This is
    - (a) above the field
    - (b) above mean sea level
    - (c) above 1013·2 mb

11. Radiation fog is more frequent in the UK in winter because
    - (a) the sky is nearly always overcast
    - (b) the wind is stronger
    - (c) the nights are longer

12. If the Environmental lapse rate is less than the Dry adiabatic lapse rate, one would expect
    - (a) altocumulus cloud
    - (b) cumulus cloud
    - (c) no cloud

13. A gale warning is issued when the average wind speed is
    - (a) 43 kt
    - (b) 34 kt
    - (c) 51 kt

14. At the dew point, the relative humidity is
    - (a) 60%
    - (b) 90%
    - (c) 100%

15. Buys Ballot's Law states
    - (a) the surface wind backs into the centre of a Low
    - (b) if you stand with your back to the wind in the Northern hemisphere the Low is on your left
    - (c) isobars are always slack in an anti-cyclone.

Answers

1. (b)	6. (c)	11. (c)
2. (b)	7. (c)	12. (c)
3. (c)	8. (b)	13. (b)
4. (c)	9. (b)	14. (c)
5. (a)	10. (a)	15. (b)

10: Aerad charts

A knowledge of these charts is emphatically not a requirement for the PPL examination, but they are in such common use that we are persuaded to include a quick run through of their more important points. From a private pilot's view, it is the detail on the sheet that is attractive. The Airways themselves, which are definite Tracks **and** 5 nm either side, are not usable without an Instrument Rating: but an Airway is classified as existing between a bottom and top level, and flying beneath it, in the conditions permitted by your licence, is allowed. And, though you will not need to report and be controlled, it is consoling to know that if things get shall we say tricky, you can call for advice and assistance from the Air Traffic Control Centre.

There are no topographical features on the chart at all; it is an aeronautical radio chart. Since a change in just one frequency among the hundreds on the sheet renders it obsolete, it can be quite a costly business keeping up to date at around a quid a throw at short irregular intervals.

Every radio station gives its call sign and frequency, and a symbol to differentiate the type of radio aid available. We'll mention most of the types but are aware that many private aircraft have a minimum of radio aboard. Along the Airways, distances are given between points, and the Track **Magnetic**. A quote is made of a safe height, too – 4·2 for example means that there is safe clearance (at 4 200 ft amsl) over obstacles of high ground within 30n. miles of the Airway and at each end of it, too. The bottom and top of the Airway is given as a sort of fraction, and here FL is quoted as usual, but if the bottom is an altitude on QNH, then the figures are set out in full.

For aircraft flying the Airway proper, a minimum Flight Level is given; Flight Information Regions (FIRs) are distinctly separated, so that they know who to report to; the order is stated as to Odd or Even thousands of feet they must fly; positions marked with a blocked-in triangle are compulsory reporting points while open triangles are 'on request' reporting points. It goes without saying that aircraft under control invariably are told to report at these points.

None of this as yet concerns you. Danger areas do, though: continuous blue lines are in effect permanently; pecked are temporary or notified to all when operative. The details of each danger area are listed against its number elsewhere on the chart, and if a height of 15 000 ft is given, say, it means mostly from the ground up to 15 000 ft, so it's advisable to treat it in this way. Days and hours of operation are sometimes noted; HN means at night from half an hour after sunset to half an hour before sunrise; HJ means heures du jour, so you've got to be educated for this game.

FIG 10.1

Isogonals are started and ended at the bottom and top of the sheet only, and the date and annual change set out in a box somewhere in an uncluttered part of the sheet. The chart's a Lambert, no Latitude divisions, so use the graduated scale line for measuring any distances.

Figure 10.1 shows the appearance of some of the matter on the Aerad chart: any relationship to actual names and frequencies is coincidental.

Start at BELWETHER, which has a non-directional beacon, call sign BLW, frequency 342 kHz. The frequency of these beacons (to which the aircraft's ADF is tuned, whereupon a pointer on a dial indicates the direction of the station) is medium, and on the charts recognisable as being whole numbers between 200 and 1750; usually in the lower hundreds in fact. The Track Magnetic is 283°, so the W/V to apply to get the Heading Magnetic must itself be the Magnetic value. The isogonal here is found by visually joining the start and end at the bottom and top, say 10W, crossing this Airway around the A3 marking.

All aircraft flying the Airway proper would report on the R/T to SISLEY Airways on 129·3 MHz. To starboard is a small circle marking a permanent danger area; whether it extends to below or above 10 000 ft is immaterial to you, since it's from the ground up and must be an ever-present peril to the private pilot at his comparatively low level. Information on R 111 could be looked up on the reverse of the chart for details of the danger. The vertical extent of the Airway (between which all aircraft are considered to be officially on it and accept control, reporting as required) is FL 250 and altitude 4 500; the base is on regional QNH, in this case, the MORDIC Altimeter Setting Region. This QNH is given by SISLEY, who will give the DUNDAS QNH before the aircraft crosses the ASR boundary.

This Airway is called A3, and the distance from BELWETHER to PORRIDGE is 82 nm, between compulsory reporting points, the filled-in triangles; on the Airway, aircraft must fly at or above FL 60. FL 60 is OK, as in this direction flight must be in Even thousands of feet. The 4·1 is 4 100 ft above mean sea level, here indicating safe terrain clearance. The danger area to port D 771, is temporary, and if active would have been notified in a 'Notice to Airmen' (Notam) in good time.

FUNDEE is an on-request reporting point, and the request is nearly always made. The ellipse here is a Fan Marker and these all work on 75 MHz, and are vertically directed beams which at 15 000 ft span the 10-mile wide Airway, giving out Morse dots, dashes or both as the aircraft passes through the fan. It's a guarantee that the aircraft is on the Airway at least; its use is simple, just a switch to be flicked on by the pilot. Coloured lights on the instrument panel are associated with it, too, but perhaps we digress, especially as the fan marker is getting rarer all the time.

Airways aircraft passing from SISLEY Airways to BRESTON must be aware of crossing the boundary in that their next report will be on BRESTON's frequency; it is no longer mandatory to report the crossing. PORRIDGE is a compulsory report point, with a Very High Frequency Omni-Range (VOR), call sign POR, frequency 112·2 MHz. This radio aid is very precise, and an aircraft tuned in gets a bearing to or from the station, a magnetic bearing at that. The frequencies range in the UK from 108 to 118 MHz, and the clock face at the station is supposed to be a help in placing bearings received; the flag indicates Magnetic North. Channel 103 is the channel to select if you're carrying Distance Measuring Equipment (DME) to get instantly, on a counter, the distance from the station.

A private pilot can use these aids, as he's not interfering with anyone. He can call SISLEY or BRESTON in emergency; and he is allowed to fly at quadrantal heights at 4 500 ft or below in Visual Flight Rules conditions. Terrain clearance and avoidance of other aircraft are his look-out. If you invest in an Aerad chart, you will get a very comprehensive and explanatory 'Legend Card' which you should keep with the chart.

11: Aviation Law

This is the subject of a separate PPL paper, and a pass mark of 70% is demanded. There's no dodging the need for a sound knowledge of the Law as laid down for the private pilot. In this section, we shall plough through the syllabus, summarising in a lucid fashion, we hope, the rules, regulations and orders for you.

VFR/IFR and that

After prolonged thought, we've decided to start this section with a few definitions. Sorry.

Visual Flight Rules (VFR), a flight conducted in accordance with visual flight rules, whereby the pilot undertakes full responsibility for the safety and navigation of his aircraft, and separation from other aircraft. There is no control from the ground, and the pilot gets no instructions from Air Traffic Control (ATC).

YOU MAY FLY VFR

IN CONTROLLED AIRSPACE provided that the following weather minima prevail:	OUTSIDE CONTROLLED AIRSPACE for flight above 3 000 feet amsl	for flight at 3 000 feet amsl or below in an aircraft other than a helicopter
1. flight visibility of 5 nm 2. cloud separation horizontally is 1 nm from the aircraft 3. cloud separation vertically is 1 000 ft above and below the aircraft	same weather as for flight in controlled airspace	1. if IAS is 140 kt or less, you keep clear of cloud, keep in sight of the surface, and have a flight visibility of at least 1 nm. 2. if IAS is more than 140 kt, you have flight visibility of at least 3 nm, keep 1 nm horizontally and 1 000 ft vertically from cloud.

Exceptions

1. Helicopters. Flying outside CAS at or below 3 000 ft amsl must remain clear of cloud and in sight of the surface *or* keep 1 nm horizontally and 1 000 ft vertically from cloud and have a flight visibility of 3 nm.

2. At night there is no VFR. All flights are conducted under IFR unless a clearance is granted for Special VFR (details to follow).

3. *Notified Airspace.* If the particular controlled airspace is 'notified for the purpose of Rule 21' – Rule 21 of the Rules of the Air and Air Traffic Control Regulations 1985 – entry into that airspace under VFR is forbidden. Thus, if it is proposed to fly through some controlled airspace or zone under VFR, the first thing to do is to check in the RAC section of the UK Air Pilot if that zone is notified for the purpose of Rule 21. If not the flight may proceed under VFR: but if it is notified, it may be necessary to obtain special clearance for VFR should IFR be out of·the question. Do you get that lot?

4. When conditions are below the VFR minima outlined above, the flight cannot take place under VFR.

When the weather is below VMC, a pilot must fly IFR, and the rules depend on the type of airspace.

Instrument Flight Rules (IFR), a flight conducted in accordance with instrument flight rules. A pilot may elect to fly IFR at any time.

Flight visibility, the visibility forward from the flight deck of an aircraft in flight.

Visual Meteorological Conditions (VMC), when there is flight visibility of 5 nm, no cloud around in the horizontal for 1 nm, and no cloud above or below the aircraft within 1 000 ft.

Instrument Meteorological Conditions (IMC), weather precluding flight in compliance with Visual Flight Rules.

VMC conditions are obligatory for VFR flight, but even that may be modified by whether the flight takes place in Controlled or Uncontrolled Airspace. We shall discuss Airspace later, but in the meantime the implications of the words are sufficient.

IFR

If the flight is INSIDE CONTROLLED AIRSPACE	If the flight is OUTSIDE CONTROLLED AIRSPACE	
The pilot must comply with the following requirements:	above 3 000 ft amsl	at 3 000 ft amsl and below
1. he must hold an Instrument Rating	1. fly at least 1 000 ft above the highest obstacle within 5 nm of the aircraft	1. fly at least 1 000 ft above the highest obstacle within 5 nm of the aircraft, unless the aircraft is clear of cloud and in sight of the surface
2. he must file a Flight Plan with the appropriate ATC	2. Exceptions to the above requirements are:	
3. he must obtain ATC clearance to proceed to or enter the airspace and obey instructions	(a) when flying under ATC instructions, or	
4. he must make position reports in accordance with notified procedures or as required by ATCC		

5. during the flight, he must maintain adequate ground clearance i.e. at least 1 000 ft clearance of the highest obstacle within 5 nm of the aircraft

(b) when in notified holding patterns or following holding procedures at an aerodrome.

It will be noticed that the requirement of 'adequate' terrain clearance applies in all circumstances when flying IFR. Of course there have to be exceptions from this requirement, otherwise, for example no aircraft can take off or land. The exceptions are as follows:

(a) an aircraft taking off or landing:
(b) an aircraft flying on a route notified for the purpose of Rule 25 (when special minimum criteria are applied):
(c) an aircraft otherwise authorised by the competent authority.

A private pilot without an IMC rating, however, cannot fly outside controlled airspace:

(i) when visibility is less than $1\frac{1}{2}$ nm, or
(ii) when any passenger is carried and the aircraft is flying either above 3 000 ft amsl in IMC or below 3 000 ft amsl in visibility of less than 3 nm.

Quadrantal/Semi-circular Height Rules
When flying outside controlled airspace in IMC, in order to comply with IFR, an aircraft in level flight must fly at the appropriate cruising level,

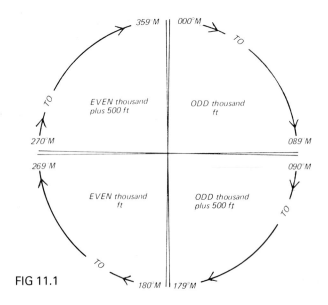

FIG 11.1

and are you quite happy about the expression 'flight level'? The levels allotted depend on the *Magnetic* Track of the aircraft.

Flight at levels below 24 500 ft
Track Magnetic 000 to 089 inc, fly at odd thousands, e.g. 5 000, 7 000 etc.

090 to 179 inc, fly at odd thousands + 500, e.g. 5 500, 7 500 etc.

180 to 269 inc, fly at even thousands, e.g. 4 000, 6 000 etc.

270 to 359 inc, fly at even thousands + 500, e.g. 4 500, 6 500 etc.

This is called the Quadrantal rule since the flight level is decided by the quadrant of the circle where the flight is taking place. Check against Fig. 11.1.

Flight at or above 24 500 ft
The following semi-circular rule applies:

Track Magnetic between 000 and 179 inc
levels available are 25 000
27 000
29 000
33 000 and every 4 000 ft thereafter

Track Magnetic between 180 and 359 inc
levels available are 26 000
28 000
31 000
35 000 and every 4 000 ft thereafter

These are all flown as flight levels with 1013·2 mb set on the altimeter sub-scale; the purpose is to provide separation between conflicting traffic in IMC. They **must** be flown when outside controlled airspace in IMC, and pilots are **advised** to fly quadrants in VFR.

In this way, 1 000 ft separation is provided under quadrantal rules for aircraft on reciprocal Tracks Magnetic; under semi-circular rules, the separation is 1 000 ft up to 29 000 ft and 2 000 ft above that.

Special VFR
You will have worked out by now that a pilot who cannot fulfil the IFR requirements cannot:

(i) enter controlled airspace in IMC or at night

(ii) enter controlled airspace by day or night no matter what the weather if the airspace is notified for the purpose of Rule 21.

(iii) enter any airspace to which Special Rules apply.

However, if he must go into the area and is unable to comply with IFR, he may apply for a Special VFR clearance. In this connection:

1. Before requesting Special VFR clearance pilots must ensure that:
   (a) they can fly at such heights as will enable them to land clear of a built-up area in the event of engine failure
   (b) the requisite flight visibility can be maintained, and
   (c) their responsibility for terrain clearance can be met.

2. Grant of such a clearance is a concession and cannot be claimed as a right.

3. If the clearance is given, the flight is conducted under the specific instructions issued by the ATC and is not flown under IFR.

4. Such flights mainly take place in control zones (story later) at low altitudes. A pilot flying special VFR under ATC instructions is not absolved from obeying the normal rule of staying 1 500 ft above highest obstructions in the vicinity of a town, city or settlement.

5. There is no need to file a flight plan (though a pilot may do so if he likes). He must give the aircraft's registration and callsign, aircraft type, his intentions, and the request for special VFR clearance.

6. ATC will provide standard separation.

7. Special VFR flights will be given a limiting upper level. The pilot must obey instructions from ATC, but he must keep in weather conditions which ensure he stays on Track and clear of obstructions.

8. Here's the rub – a private pilot will only be cleared for Special VFR if he holds an IMC rating **unless** the visibility is at least 5 nm. It's a sporting chance, then.

9. Special VFR is also available in certain Special Rules airspace where provision for such flights is made.

There are, inside control zones, a few aerodromes with entry/exit lanes for local aircraft in IMC yet not filling IFR procedures; these are Club airfields with privileges in the immediate area for student pilots. They are listed in the UK Air Pilot at the RAC section, but are of no interest to an examinee whatever.

Types of Airspace

The whole of the air round the UK is parcelled up tight in order to provide service to aircraft which must have it, or need it. The 'must have its' are aeroplanes under control, and it is the control of the British air which we study now.

Lower Airspace goes up to 24 500 ft, but not including it, and is called a Flight Information Region (FIR). There are only two FIRs in the country, London, and Scottish. From 24 500 ft itself (and that's a FL) on up is an Upper Flight Information Region (UIR), and they're at the same two places. Much the same type of division is done abroad – Paris FIR/UIR, Frankfurt FIR/UIR, etc, although the dividing flight level between FIR and UIR may not be the same.

The degree of control within the airspace is conditioned by the volume of traffic. In areas with a vast inflow and outflow of internal and international traffic there must be full control of every aircraft, with complete discipline in the area. In return, separation and the smooth flow are undertaken by ATC. Where this all happens is 'Controlled Airspace'. Where traffic is thin and restrictions are not necessary, way out in the bundu, then we have 'Uncontrolled Airspace'.

The next step in Controlled Airspace is division according to local circumstances. At London Airport, for example, there is continuous movement of aircraft at all heights in all directions, and Control is vital over all traffic to a distance well away from the field itself. At all such places a Control Zone is set up. A Control Zone (CTR) extends from ground level to a specified altitude, or flight level, and gives air traffic control service to IFR flights. A CTR may be wholly or partially notified for the purpose of Rule 21, and details are in the RAC section of the UK Air Pilot, or have we said that before? There's no control service for VFR flights, which are only permitted to enter those Control Zones not notified for Rule 21. Under present regulations, you won't get into the largish area of the London CTR below FL 110. As a result, the turmoil which many foreign fields endure because of the free access of unscheduled aircraft is avoided. Of course, details like this are not part of the examination syllabus.

The follow-up to Control Zones is the area of actual flight on busy routes, the control of aircraft at flight level. These are 'Control Areas', the service is the same to IFR flights, and the area extends from a specified altitude or flight level without an upper limit unless specified; we're still in Controlled Airspace. Control Areas comprise:

Airways, which extend as laid down in the rules for Control Areas; they are all notified for Rule 21, so there's no VFR traffic on them.

Terminal Control Areas (TMAs), which are established at the confluence of airways in the vicinity of busy aerodromes, and their purpose is to sort out transit from landing/departing traffic. Transit traffic is kept away from the field itself.

Moving to Uncontrolled Airspace, there are occasionally areas where the volume of traffic warrants some sort of service, such as flight separation, but no more. These are called **Advisory Service Areas** (ASA), and this partial service is available to aircraft voluntarily accepting it. Routes are sometimes advised to be taken, Advisory Routes (ADR), much the same as airways, but corridors without the advantages and compulsions.

No control service is supplied in ASA, but if the advisory service is required, then an IFR flight plan must be filed; this will ensure Flight Information service and flight separation from known traffic.

Then there are **Special Rules Areas** and **Special Rules Zones**. A special Rules Area is defined as an area within an FIR/UIR within which aircraft are required to comply with the instructions of the ATC. They extend from a specified alt/FL and have an upper limit. A Special Rules Zone is defined similarly except that it extends from Ground level to a specified alt/FL. In this type of airspace special rules peculiar to the area/zone apply, e.g. entry permission, R/T listening watch, position reporting and so forth.

In all Uncontrolled Airspace, Flight Information Service is normally available, and this is discussed later; at all airfields an Air Traffic Control Service operates within the airfield boundary.

Run through this chapter of essential knowledge with another of our famous tabulations:

Types of Air Traffic Service Units
We now review the general system of organisation in the UK for controlling traffic.

Air Traffic Control Centre (ATCC) provides service to aircraft within its area in controlled or uncontrolled airspace, and Flight Information Service and alerting service. So an ATCC provides:

(a) Flight information service and alerting service
(b) Advisory service to all aircraft under IFR in ASAs and on ADRs.
(c) Area control service to aircraft on Airways and in TMAs.
(d) Area control service in some of the larger zones.

The extent of ATCC service may be clarified by Fig 11.2, opposite.

Zone Control Units are sometimes established in zones of medium importance to control aircraft in the zone – but not take-off or landing.

Aerodrome Control. There are two sections really; the Approach Control Unit which deals with approach services to aircraft landing and taking off in IFR; while the Aerodrome Control Unit looks after all aircraft at the aerodrome, on the ground or flying purely locally, out of the jurisdiction of the Approach Control Unit in other words.

It is rather a maze of tags and labels, but it's worth a few readings to get the diffs. An aircraft taking off from an aerodrome inside a zone gets the following changes of control:

> aerodrome control
> approach control
> zone control
> ATCC during flight in TMA if one's there
> ATCC on the airway.

FIG 11.2

Unlicensed Air Traffic Control. At certain aerodromes where the full air traffic service is not available, an aerodrome information service may be provided by a licensed Aerodrome Flight Information Service Officer (AFISO). As the title suggests, the service provided is essentially an information service, and is available when flying inside an aerodrome ATZ. The responsibilities of an AFISO are these:

(a) Issuing information to aircraft flying in the Aerodrome Traffic Zone (ATZ) to assist pilots in preventing collisions.

(b) Issuing information to aircraft on the manoeuvring area or between aircraft moving on the apron.

(c) Informing aircraft of the state of the aerodrome and its facilities.

(d) Initiating overdue action.

It will be appreciated that there are still aerodromes where neither control service nor the information service is available. The control tower and its radio at such aerodromes only serve the purpose of providing air-/ground communication.

At aerodromes where full ATC service is provided, the callsign is, as appropriate, Tower, Approach, Ground, Zone or Radar. Where AFIS is being offered the callsign is '... information' and where no ATC or AFIS is available, the callsign is '... Radio'.

Summary so far

1. If you are VMC, you may fly VFR in controlled airspace (unless notified for Rule 21), and in uncontrolled airspace.

2. There is no VFR at night in the UK.

3. In IMC you must fly IFR in controlled airspace. Outside controlled airspace, you must fly quadrantals if above 3 000 ft. Note all the other requirements of IFR.

4. Within the two FIR/UIRs, there are two divisions: controlled and uncontrolled airspace. Airways and TMAs are controlled areas, which with control zones constitute controlled airspace.

5. In uncontrolled airspace, there are advisory areas and routes where separation service is provided to aircraft on IFR flight plan. Special Rules restrictions apply to flights in Special Rules airspace.

6. The three ATCCs provide communication service on an area basis to aircraft flying in controlled and uncontrolled airspace, and control service in large zones. They are the lynch-pin of the whole scheme, and will pass an aircraft the order to transfer to zone, approach control, etc.

Altimeter Setting Procedures

In Chapter 9 on Meteorology, altimeter settings were run through, with their Q code references. In the PPL exam, questions on this material will turn up in the Navigation and Met paper, and the Law paper; some of what follows may be repetitive, confined to points where stress is valuable, but the main concern right now is procedures.

A fine point in QFE, when the altimeter reads **height** above the aerodrome in flight and zero feet on the field itself, is where to measure the barometric pressure on an un-level surface. The datum point is the aerodrome elevation, the highest point on the manoeuvring area, which is any part of the field where the movement of aircraft is provided for, excluding the apron and maintenance areas. Runways are considered part of the manoeuvring area, but the highest point on the field – and thus taken as the QFE datum – may well be a spot on the perimeter away from the runway.

QNH gives **altitude**, and it's ATC or ATCC who give the 'Regional QNH' for the ASRs. This lowest forecast regional QNH, you recall, is changed on the hour, valid for the ensuing hour, but can be obtained up to one hour ahead of the current hour – a boon to pilots on a long cross-country without radio. So QNH is reset on the hour or when entering a new ASR. All QNHs obtained by radio must be repeated back.

QNE, strictly the altimeter indication on landing with 1013·2 set on the sub-scale, but generally spoken of as the 1013·2 setting, looks after flight separation, and all quadrantals and semi circulars are flown on this setting as FLs, which are referred to minus the last two zeros, e.g. FL 90 is Flight Level 9 000 ft on an altimeter sub-scale setting of 1013·2 mb.

So it's height above a specified datum (QFE), altitude above mean sea level (QNH), level above 1013·2 mb on the sub-scale (QNE).

There are some further particular terms and procedures used in take-off and landing, as well as in receiving instructions and in giving reports. We take the terms first, and go on in orderly fashion to the procedures in and out of controlled airspace.

Transition altitude is the altitude in the vicinity of an aerodrome at or below which the vertical position of an aircraft is controlled by reference to altitude. Outside controlled airspace in the UK, it is generally 3 000 ft; in control zones, an effort is made to establish a common transition altitude for all aerodromes.

Transition Level is the lowest level available for use above the transition altitude.

Transition Layer is the airspace between the transition altitude and the transition level. In the transition layer, climbing aircraft report their vertical position in terms of FL, but descending aircraft report in terms of altitude – to make the pilot think ahead perhaps.

Check with the Fig. 11.3.

FIG 11.3

A little sum may not be out of place here, it makes for variety. An aircraft takes off with aerodrome QNH 1003 mb set in the sub-scale and keeps it till the transition altitude 3 000 ft is reached. Obeying the rules, the pilot adjusts the sub-scale to read 1013·2. This turning up of the setting at once increases the dial reading by roughly 10 × 30, 30 ft being a mean value per millibar. The altimeter now reads 3 300 ft, and the transition layer is 200 ft thick for him to reach the transition level of 3 500 ft, or FL 35.

Procedures

Before leaving the briefing room and the Met Office at the departure field, the height to fly will have been decided. This will be stated as a FL or altitude as appropriate, and it's important if it's a FL that adequate terrain clearance is ensured, that all Control requirements are met, and that it complies with the quadrantals or semi-circulars on every leg on the trip.

Rules within Controlled Airspace

1. Take-off: one altimeter set to QNH, and this is the aerodrome QNH.
2. Climb. Report altitude to the transition altitude, then flight levels.
3. En route, Fly flight levels at and above transition altitude. The regional QNH is used en route for terrain clearance purposes, but it should be noted that in CTR/TMA at or below transition altitude, the aircraft's altimeter is set to the **aerodrome** QNH given at the field prior to take-off.
4. Approach and Landing.
   (a) Set aerodrome QNH when cleared to descend unless further reports are called for (these would be FLs until transition level); in any case, aerodrome QNH must be set just before transition level.
   (b) On final approach, set QFE or QNH. On a radar approach, QFE is assumed – it's the norm for the pilot doing the landing, but nothing to stop a pilot preferring airfield QNH.
   (c) Remember that Obstacle Clearance Limit (OCL) is always given with reference to runway touchdown or aerodrome elevation.
5. Missed Approach. No need to alter the altimeter setting unless a report of vertical position is called for; this must be in terms of altitude, so it's pretty general to flick to QNH for the circuit.

Rules outside Controlled Airspace

1. Take-off and initial climb. Any desired setting.
2. Flight at or below 3 000 ft.
   (a) Any desired setting, but any reports of vertical position must be in terms of altitude.
   (b) On an ADR, regional QNH must be set.
   (c) When flying beneath TMA and Special Rules Areas (SRAs), use

the QNH of an aerodrome situated beneath those areas when flying below the transition altitude.

3. Flight above 3 000 ft. Change to 1013·2 mb on passing the transition altitude when flying under IFR and conform to the quadrantal rule. Reports in flight level terms.

4. Approach and landing. As for controlled airspace.

5. Missed Approach. Ditto, as for missed approach in controlled airspace.

6. Flight in TMAs. When arriving or departing from aerodromes in TMA when at or below transition altitude, set aerodrome QNH, not regional.

You will find after a few readings and getting acquainted with the various terms, the settings make sense. A couple of titbits to close with.

Pre-flight altimeter checks are done on the apron at start-up as part of the normal checks on the aircraft. The apron elevations are exhibited in the briefing room, as well as published in the UK Air Pilot.

Altimeter setting values are passed by ATC to the pilot over the radio, rounded down to the nearest whole millibar. On request, and it's frequently made, aerodrome pressure setting to the nearest tenth of a millibar will be given.

Aeronautical Information Service

The publication documenting all matters concerning air operations in the UK is called the 'Air Pilot', and the layout is standard, so that it is easy to find one's way around the Air Information Publication of other countries. It is the official document for 'notifying' the requirements of aviation legislation, i.e. as set forth in a document issued by the Civil Aviation Authority and entitled Notam–UK or UK Air Pilot. The eight sections of the Air Pilot, some of which we will look at further, are:

AGA: aerodromes, all the details, services available, customs, lighting, even safe obstacle clearances within 25 nm.

COM: aerodrome and en route radio communication and navigation services over the whole country.

MET: met organisation, procedures, broadcasts, codes, lists of offices.

RAC: rules of flight in types of airspace, altimeter setting requirements, airmiss report procedures, filing of flight plans, in fact anything connected with operational flying in the UK.

FAL: is short for facilitation, arrival and departure procedures, documentation, customs, health formalities.

SAR: search and rescue organisation and procedures.

MAP: mainly lists of maps and charts available.

GEN: oddments, notes on time system, units used, aircraft registration marks, list of legislation.

The Air Pilot is kept up to date by monthly supplements. The whole thing is bulky and expensive, the supplements are expensive, and the job of amendment infinitely tedious. Do not buy it unless you're buying an airfield. Not likely to be found in your local reference library either.

Notams. These are Notices to Airmen, to pass on temporary warnings of a navigational nature, such as an active danger area; they're not by any chalk amendments to the Air Pilot, but additions or alterations for the time being. A Class II notam is nothing much, and is sent by post, but a Class I is urgent and is sent out over the Aeronautical Fixed Telecommunication Network (AFTN). Notams marked 'Airac' are advance notices of changes which will take place in 4 weeks time on a Thursday (by international agreement); they refer to any operational matter, such as a change in noise abatement procedures at some aerodrome, frequency changes, alteration in siting of aids, etc.

Information Circulars. Monthly details of an administrative nature, often about maps and charts, but also times of licence exams, amendments to syllabi, availability of official publications. A pink one is about a safety aspect, full of critical and valuable information.

The Aeronautical Information Service (AIS). This section of the Civil Aviation Authority collects aeronautical information, puts it in order, and spreads it around to everyone who should have it. At centres like London, Manchester and Prestwick, full coverage of UK information is held, and plenty of the information of and from foreign parts; these centres also initiate Class I notams. Aerodrome Units maintain varying degrees of information depending on the type and volume of traffic.

Aerodromes

We plunge straight in to a resumé of matter relevant to your exam; details of particular aerodromes are not of course required, but they are all in the AGA section.

General limitations. Only in genuine emergency are aircraft permitted to land at any aerodrome not listed in the UK Air Pilot. Special permission to land at unlisted or disused aerodromes may be granted in exceptional circumstances, such as uplifting a sick person or carrying out a task of national importance.

CAA aerodromes can be freely used in published working hours; at other times only with prior permission.

Aerodrome Licence, Ordinary. Use of an aerodrome operating under this licence is by prior permission of the owner.

Unlicensed Aerodromes. Use by prior permission of the owner.

Service Aerodromes. The use of these is really uptight. Check if the one you want to use is available for civil use, then check on the limitations of traffic, such as type of aircraft permitted. Then get the authority of the Station Commander before, repeat, before you take-off. And bear in mind the following:

1. Report to the ATC on arrival and before leaving.
2. Hangarage is only provided after Service requirements are met.
3. The Service undertakes no responsibility for messing or accommodation; the pilot may make his own arrangements for the supply of fuel, oil, etc., after furnishing adequate cover against loss or damage to Service property through the use of equipment.
4. The Service undertakes no liability for loss, damage or accident to the visitor's person or property.
5. The use of Service apparatus, tractors, cranes, starter trolleys, etc. is at the user's risk.
6. Pilots making instrument approaches will be given OCL based on QFE.
7. Control of entry procedures apply to civil aircraft.
8. Two-way R/T must be maintained, usually on 122·1. The VHF Emergency frequency of 121·5 must not be regarded as the common frequency. Aircraft with no R/T may be treated exceptionally at the discretion of the Commanding Officer.
9. At RN stations available for use by civil aircraft, all main and standby runways are equipped with wire arrester gear. The wires, which are unmarked, should not present a hazard to an aircraft taxiing slowly provided there is a minimum clearance of 12 inches from the ground to the lowest part of the aircraft. Landing and take-off can be restricted to the runway between the wires.

Aeronautical Ground Lights at civil and military aerodromes are as follows:

(a) Identification beacons; flash a 2-letter ident every 12 seconds at a speed of about 6 to 8 words a minute; red for Service aerodromes, green for civil.

(b) Aerodrome beacons; an alternating white and green light on or near the aerodrome. Never installed at Service aerodromes and rarely at civil fields which have an ident beacon going. At civil aerodromes, beacons normally operate in bad visibility by day and at the discretion of the air traffic controller by night, though this discretion is not granted at certain aerodromes and the beacons work nightly from sunset to sunrise. At Service master aerodromes, beacons operate nightly; at other Service fields, they operate to meet local requirements.

The Morse code idents of all beacons in the UK, and details of colour are in the AGA section.

A couple of definitions to close this section:

Aerodrome elevation is the highest point on the manoeuvring area – we warned you some of this chapter would be repetitive; all aerodromes have their elevations listed in the AGA section.

Alternate Aerodrome is an aerodrome selected prior to take-off to which the flight may proceed when a landing at the intended destination becomes inadvisable.

The Flight Plan

This is a message prepared by the pilot and handed in for transmission to the organisations concerned with the flight and for obtaining a clearance for the flight to proceed. It contains all the essential information about the flight such as callsign, estimated time of departure, route details and times between reporting points, TAS, radio frequencies carried, survival equipment on board and so on.

1. **When to file a flight plan?**
   (a) A pilot may file a flight plan for any flight, irrespective of whether it is IFR or VFR, in controlled airspace or outside.
   (b) A pilot **must** file a flight plan:
      (i) When the flight takes place in controlled airspace in IMC or at night.
      (ii) When a pilot elects to fly IFR in controlled airspace when he could have flown VFR.
      (iii) When a flight is conducted in controlled airspace notified for the purpose of Rule 21. There's no VFR in this airspace.
      (iv) If a pilot on an advisory route wishes to use Advisory Service, a flight plan must be filed despite the fact that the advisory airspace is not controlled airspace.
      (v) When a pilot on Special VFR wishes the destination aerodrome to be informed of his movements.
      (vi) If he intends to fly in certain Special Rules Areas/Zones irrespective of weather conditions.
      (vii) For any flight from the UK which will cross the UK FIR boundary.
      (viii) For all flights within the Scottish and London Upper FIRs.
      (ix) For any flight from a UK aerodrome to a destination more than 40 km away and the maximum total weight authorised exceeds 5 700 kg.
   (c) A pilot **is advised** to file a flight plan:
      (i) When planning a flight that is likely to go beyond 10 nm of the UK coast.
      (ii) When the flight is made over sparsely populated or mountainous areas, when radio equipment is not carried.

2. **How to file a flight plan.** You may file the flight plan at the departure aerodrome. In this case, complete form CA 48 in triplicate (it's already

carbonned) at least 30 minutes before clearance to start up or taxy is requested, and hand it in to the local Air Traffic Control. He'll keep the top copy, the middle one is for the teleprinter operator, and you're left with the bottom copy on which nothing is legible except perhaps the controller's signature.

Always give as much notice as possible when filing a Flight Plan. The minimum time goes up from 30 minutes to 1 hour if Controlled Airspace, Advisory Airspace, etc, is involved. It is most important that the Flight Plan is correctly completed to ensure that it can be handled under the automatic data processing system. Failure to do so may result in a delayed flight. Full instructions on the completion of Flight Plans are given in a yellow AIC. The AIC even has an Appendix giving 'Typical Errors' to be avoided!

If the departure aerodrome is not on AFTN, then the pilot may telephone the flight plan to the parent unit; in this case, arrangements must be made to pass the actual take-off and airborne times to the same unit.

Alternatively, a pilot may file a flight plan while airborne. The message must commence 'I wish to file an airborne flight plan' and be addressed to the FIR controller or failing that to any Air Traffic Service unit. In general, airborne flight plans are filed when it is decided to enter controlled airspace not originally planned, and the filing must be made at least 10 minutes before entry is required.

3. Deviation from plan. If a pilot decides to land elsewhere, he must inform ATCC/FIR as soon as possible, subsequently giving details of the new route. In any case, he must inform the original destination within 30 minutes of his ETA there, otherwise search will be initiated.

4. Cancellation of IFR. A pilot may request cancellation of IFR flight plan when in controlled airspace provided he can maintain VMC and the airspace is not notified for Rule 21. The message is 'callsign, cancel IFR flight plan'. ATC cannot approve or disapprove such a request, but will advise the pilot if he is likely to meet IMC later in the flight. A mere report that a pilot is VMC does **not** constitute cancellation of an IFR flight plan.

5. Booking in and out. Every pilot going flying is required to 'book out' at the aerodrome ATS unit. A booking out does not constitute filing a flight plan, but when a flight plan is filed, a separate booking out is not required. Similarly, a pilot who has just made a flight is required to 'book in' at the aerodrome ATS unit.

Flight at aerodromes

We must confess that this section contains some hard swot; the ground signals must be well learnt.

There's no need to define an aerodrome, but round each aerodrome a traffic zone is established – 'the airspace extending from the aerodrome to 2 000 ft above it and within a distance of $1\frac{1}{2}$ nm of its boundaries, except any part of that airspace which is within the traffic zone of another aerodrome which is notified for the purpose of the Air Navigation Order 1985 as being the controlling Aerodrome'.

Some aerodromes, the busier ones, have Special Rule Zones. Their dimensions are arranged to suit local requirements, set out in Rule 36 of the Rules of the Air and Air Traffic Regulations 1985. Remember that these SRZs can only be entered with prior permission which must be sought at least 10 minutes before entry is wanted.

Certain military airfields have established Military Aerodrome Traffic Zones (MATZ), the airspace up to 3 000 ft above the aerodrome within 5 nm radius of the Aerodrome Reference Point. A stub sticks out lined up with the centre line of the final approach path 5 nm long and a couple of miles either side of it; this can be varied for the type of flying normally engaged in. Most MATZ participate in a penetration scheme for civil aircraft; an aircraft would call the controlling field 'Bricket Wood, this is G AJEL, request MATZ penetration' 15 nm or 5 minutes flying time from the boundary, whichever is the greater and when satisfactory R/T is established, follow up with further information of aircraft type, position, heading, altitude, flight conditions, departure aerodrome, destination aerodrome, position of entry, ETA and TAS. Thereafter, obey instructions, maintain listening watch and advise the controller when clear of the zone. The setting of the altimeter is aerodrome QFE (if two MATZ are combined the QFE of the higher is passed as the 'clutch' QFE). Separation is provided to all such aircraft, but there is no compulsion about the procedures, so keep a close lookout. Always call the MATZ controller at the regulation distance; if it's open, you have the safety of control, if it's shut, you have the satisfaction of knowing you're free of their aircraft but still proceed with caution.

Visual Signals at aerodromes. These standard signals are displayed in a signals area near the air traffic building for the instruction of all aircraft, especially those without radio. Their appearances and meanings follow:

1. Direction of Landing. A white T is displayed in the signals area to show the direction of landing; landing is parallel to the shaft of the T towards the cross bar. Fig. 11.4.

2. Landing Prohibited. A red square panel with yellow diagonals. Fig. 11.5.

3. Special Precautions. A red square panel with a single yellow diagonal only, signifies that the state of the manoeuvring area is poor and special care must be taken when landing. Fig. 11.6.

4. Use hard surface only. A white dumb-bell. Fig. 11.7.

5. Take-off and land on the runway, ground movement not confined to hard surface. A black strip on each circular portion of the dumb-bell, at right angles to the shaft. Fig. 11.8.

FIG 11.4   FIG 11.5   FIG 11.6

FIG 11.7   FIG 11.8

6. Direction of take-off and landing not necessarily the same. A black ball suspended from a mast, **and** a white disc placed along the cross arm of the T. Fig. 11.9.

7. Right hand circuit in progress. A red and yellow striped arrow pointing in a clockwise direction; a green flag may also be flown from a mast. Fig. 11.10.

FIG 11.9

FIG 11.10

FIG 11.11

FIG 11.12   FIG 11.13

8. Glider flying in progress. A double white cross and/or two red balls suspended from a mast. A yellow cross indicates the tow-rope dropping area. Fig. 11.11.

9. Helicopter operations. Where helicopters are required to take off and land only within a designated area, a white letter H is displayed. Another and larger H indicates the area to be used by helicopters.

10. Landing area for light aircraft. A white letter L indicates a part of the manoeuvring area which shall be used only for the take off and landing of light aircraft. A red letter L displayed on the dumb-bell signifies that light aircraft are permitted to take off and land either on the runway or on the area designated by the white letter L.

11. Runway indication. Black numerals in two-letter groups, e.g. 28, meaning that the magnetic direction of the runway in use is 280°.

12. Aerodrome Control in operation. A checkered flag or board containing 12 equal squares coloured red and yellow alternately, signifies that the aircraft may move on the manoeuvring area and apron only with the permission, and on the instructions of, the air traffic control unit at the aerodrome. Fig. 11.12.

13. Reporting Point. A black letter C against a yellow background indicates the position where a pilot can report to the air traffic control unit. It doesn't have to be the tower.

14. Unserviceable portion of runway or taxyway. Two or more white crosses displayed on a runway/taxyway with the arms of the crosses at 45° to the centreline of the runway indicates that the portion enclosed is unserviceable (u/s). The crosses are not placed more than 300 m apart, and are visible from the air. To guide taxying aircraft, orange and white markers are placed not more than 15 m apart at the boundary of the unfit area.

15. Unserviceable portion of unpaved manoeuvring area. This is marked off by orange and white striped triangular markers, alternating with flags showing equal orange and red triangles. Fig. 11.13.

16. Aerodrome boundary markings. Striped triangular markers, orange and white, placed not more than 45 m apart. On structures, similar flat markers are used.

17. Boundary of unpaved runway. White flat rectangular markers flush with the surface.

18. Holding position. A broken white line and a continuous white line close together across a taxiway mark the point beyond which no part of an aircraft or vehicle can project towards the runway without ATC permission.

Visual light/pyrotechnic signals at aerodromes. The pilot of an aircraft, irrespective of whether it carries radio or not, may receive instructions by visual light/pyrotechnic signals; the signals and their meanings follow:

Signal	Meaning to a/c on ground	Meaning to a/c in the air
1. Intermittent green	Authorises movement on the manoeuvring area and apron	Return to the circuit or remain in the circuit and await signal for permission to land
2. Continuous green	Authorises take off	Authorises landing
3. Intermittent red	Move clear of landing strip immediately	Land elsewhere, the aerodrome is unfit or not permitted for landing
4. Continuous red	Movement prohibited	Give way to other aircraft and continue circling
5. Intermittent white	Return to your starting point	Land here after getting green light and then, after getting green flashes, proceed to the apron
6. Red pyro light or flare		Landing prohibited for the time being; any previous permission is cancelled

Similarly, an aircraft may communicate with the ATC by means of visual light/pyro signals as follows:

Signal	Meaning
1. Red pyro light or flare	Immediate assistance is requested
2. Green flashes or continuous green light or green pyro light	By night: May I land? By day: May I land in different direction from that shown by the landing T?
3. White flashes or white pyro lights or switching on and off of navigation lights or switching on and off of landing lights	I am compelled to land

Regulation of Traffic at aerodromes. Control is split between the Aerodrome Controller and the Approach Controller.

Departing aircraft are given taxy instructions, altimeter setting, take-off clearance, etc. Arriving aircraft are given their turn to land, runway in use, altimeter setting, W/V, obstruction information, taxy instructions after landing, etc. If an approach control service is operating to IFR flights, this latter packet of information is given by the approach controller.

Visual circuit is illustrated in Fig. 11.14.

FIG 11.14

Call downwind when abeam the upwind end of the runway.

Call Base leg if requested by ATC immediately on completion of the turn onto Base leg.

Call Final after completion of the turn on to final approach and when at a range of not more than 4 nm from the approach end of the runway.

Call Long Final when making a straight-in approach, or a normal approach beyond 4 nm range, up to 8 nm. Again call Final when a range of 4 nm is reached.

Use of Runways. Normally, only one aircraft may land at a time. However, another aircraft may land before the previous aircraft has cleared the runway, provided it's day time, the runway's long enough to hold them both, and the preceding aircraft is visible to the following one while it's still on the runway during the landing of the second; all these conditions must be complied with.

When two aircraft are cleared to land on the same runway, ATC will instruct 'land after ... (aircraft)' instead of 'clear to land'. It is then up to the pilot to decide how far away behind the first aircraft to land.

Local air traffic unit will nominate a runway for use which it thinks best suited to conditions. However, a pilot may request another, if he wants to.

On take-off, 'cleared to immediate take-off' means taxy to the end of the runway, take off without further ado; if already at the end of the runway, take off without delay.

Closure of aerodromes. An air traffic controller may close a CAA or public-licensed aerodrome:

(a) if the landing area is unfit

(b) when the closure is published in a Notam

(c) when essential facilities have failed; essential facilities will be interpreted in the light of existing circumstances.

An air traffic controller has no authority to close an aerodrome simply for weather reasons. Arriving aircraft have weather from broadcasts, ATCC, or the aerodrome control, and it is up to the pilot to decide to continue or divert. The first aircraft arriving at a bad weather aerodrome will be cleared to make an approach by the message 'No delay expected'. If he hangs around for the weather to improve, subsequent aircraft will be welcomed with 'Delay not determined'. These aircraft will be assigned a level in the holding stack but any may request permission to try an approach. If this is permitted, the controller will pass descent and routing instructions to clear the stack, and give an Expected Approach Time (EAT).

Flight Information Service. An Aerodrome Flight Information Service operates at certain aerodromes where no approach or control service has been established. This is not an equivalent to the Air Traffic Service. Pilots will be given the information they require, but will have to take their own decisions when flying in the area, and provide their own separation. The overriding ATCC for the area will provide Air Traffic Service and originate messages. Pilots should query any instruction which does not state its origin. And since Flight Information Service is not a fully fledged Air Traffic Service, a landing T will not be displayed in the signals area.

General Rules

The rules of flight within Aerodrome Traffic Zones depend on the type of aerodrome. At government aerodromes (e.g. military aerodromes) permission is required for take-off or landing at all times except in an emergency. For a flight within such ATZ, again, the permission of the person in charge, ATC or AFISO, is necessary at all times. If the pilot has radio on board, he must give his position and height when entering or leaving the ATZ, and while inside the airspace he must listen out.

At aerodromes owned or managed by the Authority, Licensed Aerodromes and aerodromes having ATC or AFIS units, take-off and landing (except in an emergency) is by permission at all times, but a flight through ATZ requires permission only during the notified times. The rules regarding use of radio when carried are similar to flight in a government ATZ as described above.

At any aerodrome other than the type mentioned above, permission is not required for flight in ATZ, or for take-off or landing, but movement on the aerodrome is still by prior permission.

Aerodromes not having ATC unit or AFIS. On arrival, join the circuit if one has formed and conform with the pattern. Make all turns to the left unless ground signals direct otherwise, and take-off and land in obedience to ground signals. If no signals are displayed, conform to good aviation practice, which is another way of saying it's your decision.

If take-off and landing is not on the runway:

(a) when landing, leave clear on the left any aircraft which has already landed or is landing

(b) after landing, turn left, check the coast is clear, and taxy out of the landing area

(c) when taking-off, leave clear on the left any aircraft which is already taking-off or is about to do so.

Flight in other types of Airspace

We include here only those which are pertinent to your type of flying and your syllabus of instruction.

Flight in Control Zones and TMAs demands the reporting of position under IFR (Rule 28 of the Rules of the Air and Air Traffic Regs 1985). Certain CTRs and portions of TMAs are notified for the purpose of Rule 21 which forbids entry under VFR no matter how good the weather. The designation of the Controlling Authority of a zone depends on its size, complexity and volume of traffic. At a small zone, the approach control can look after the task; at a larger, a zone controller controls the zone traffic, while in the largest, the ATCC does it. The overall controlling authority for TMA is normally the ATCC.

Permission to enter a zone must be made at least ten minutes before desired time of entry in the standard manner:

(a) callsign of aircraft

(b) aircraft type

(c) position, heading, level or altitude, flight conditions

(d) departure and destination aerodromes

(e) ETA at the point of entry

(f) TAS.

And if the entry point of the CTR or TMA is more than 10 minutes flying time from the FIR boundary, what do you think? – ask permission to enter CTR or TMA as soon as possible after crossing the FIR boundary. Should the aerodrome of departure be less than 10 minutes flying time away, clearance must be obtained before take-off.

Pilots wishing to enter CTR under VFR when the destination weather is below VFR, should contact the zone controller before entering the zone, and give notice of arrival.

Entry into CTR/TMAs notified for the purpose of Rule 21 is by prior clearance only, unless there are mitigating factors like special local flying rules or entry/exit lane procedures, when certain exemptions from full compliance with IFR rules are granted.

Flight on Airways. We've already stressed that Airways are notifed for Rule 21. There are a few further points you should know as well as some we don't mind repeating.

Crossing an Airway:
1. Cross at right angles without permission at the base, where the lower limit is defined as a Flight Level.
2. Otherwise file a flight plan before departure or while airborne, and request crossing clearance 10 minutes before ETA. As usual, the message has a laid-down format:
    (a) callsign
    (b) aircraft type
    (c) position and heading
    (d) present flight level/altitude
    (e) present flight conditions
    (f) place of crossing
    (g) crossing level
    (h) time of crossing.
3. Unless requested otherwise, stay on FIR frequency
4. Gliders may cross any airway in VMC by day without compliance with any IFR rules (not Purple Airways, though, Royal flights).
5. Other penetration by powered aircraft may be made with ATC permission. Aircraft may cross an airway in VMC by day without compliance with full IFR, but clearance must be obtained from ATCC as appropriate and the pilot must hold a valid Instrument Rating.
6. In emergency, cross at an intermediate 500 ft level.

Flight levels on airways are allotted on semi-circular rules and not on quadrantals. Broadly, flight levels at **odd** thousands of feet are flown on Tracks having an easterly element, **evens** having a westerly element.

Airways in general are corridors marked by radio navigation aids; they are control areas, or parts of control areas, of the three ATCCs. Width 10 nm, i.e. 5 nm on each side of the centre line. They are identified by colour and number, red, amber, blue, green, white; in the UK, a purple is temporary for the duration of a Royal Flight.

Flight in Flight Information Regions. An **FIR** goes up to FL 245; at that level and above, it's an Upper Flight Information Region (UIR). There are only two **FIR/UIRs** in the UK, London and Scottish. It is mandatory to carry secondary radar for flight in an **UIR**; secondary radar demands special equipment aboard which automatically replies to ground transmission. **The FIR Controller** is established at the ATCC, and provides Flight Information Service, alerting service, and some supplementary service to aircraft in the **FIR** which is outside the controlled airspace, but he does not exercise positive control over aircraft, nor issues clearances; the pilot gets information and service, but retains the initiative.

The **Flight Information Service** (FIS) gives information on the following topics.
(a) Met warnings
(b) Met conditions at destination and alternate
(c) Met reports, e.g. VFR possible along the flight path
(d) Airfield serviceability
(e) Airfield facilities
(f) Other information pertinent to the safety of navigation.

The FIR will in addition provide such **supplementary** service as:
(a) Obtain clearances to join or cross airways; the pilot stays with FIR on R/T unless ordered otherwise.
(b) Pass ETAs
(c) Accept airborne flight plans
(d) Give warnings of proximity hazards; as, outside controlled airspace and advisory airspace, aircraft can be milling around without communicating with ATS.

A request for FIR service is made in standard form: callsign, aircraft type, position and heading, FL/altitude, flight conditions, aerodrome of departure, route, destination and TAS. And, finally, for **flight outside Controlled Airspace,** what amounts to a *cri de coeur* to private pilots to avoid flying parallel or near to an airway or at its base where the base is defined as a flight level. There's much food for thought and much good sense in that admonition; where are you at 4 000 ft on QNH 1018 near an airway whose base is FL 40?

Airspace Restrictions

There are many areas in the UK which are signified as Danger, Restricted or Prohibited Areas as far as flying is concerned.

A Danger Area is an airspace of defined dimensions within which activities dangerous to the flight of an aircraft may exist at specified times. They are generally areas where captive balloons fly and weapon ranges operate. A chart of Danger Areas is issued by the CAA, and the RAC section of the UK Air Pilot contains one, with additional information. A point to note about Danger Areas is that the RAC section of the UK AIP contains details of only those Danger Areas which have an upper limit in excess of 500 ft agl. Also, some of these danger areas impose statutory prohibition of entry – these are appropriately annotated in the AIP. Amendments to them are made in the aeronautical information circulars and Class II notams. Danger areas are active to varying degrees, of course, and an effort has been made on the Danger Area chart to provide an easy reference in colour; do not confuse this chart with the colour legend on any other map or chart such as the Aerad. The one we're on about is a biggish job, stuck on the wall of a Briefing Room, against which airborne charts are checked.

Areas enclosed in **solid red**: permanently active during published hours
pecked red: inactive unless notified by Class I notam.

Restricted Areas are airspace of defined dimensions (this legal style is catching) where flight is restricted according to certain specified conditions. They usually extend from ground level to 2 000 ft agl, but there are exceptions; thus, limited penetration is allowed. Areas enclosed in solid purple on the above chart are restricted areas.

A Prohibited Area on the other hand, while usually having the same dimensions, forbids aircraft penetration absolutely. Atomic Energy establishments, for example, are prohibited to flight below 2 000 ft agl within a radius of 2 nm. Areas enclosed in solid purple on the above chart also indicate prohibited areas.

Bird Sanctuaries. These are indicated in solid green.

Air Navigation Obstructions, whatever their nature, are listed in the UKAP if they exceed 300 ft agl; if the obstruction is 500 ft or more agl, it is lighted (red). Some are lighted similarly between 300 ft and 500 ft agl. Some hills are lighted. The CAA does not accept responsibility for any obstructions which aren't listed or lit; someone has to inform them, they say.

Other hazards to flight are detailed in the UK Air Pilot, e.g. glider tow-rope dropping from 1 500 ft; pilotless aircraft which fly up to 60 000 ft; balloons for parachute training up to 1 000 ft; high speed flying areas.

In connection with aircraft approaching any area where flying is restricted or prohibited by reason of the national defence or any other reasons affecting the public interest, the following signals have the warning, and call for action, as given:

In the United Kingdom, by day or by night, a series of projectiles fired from the ground at intervals of 10 seconds, each showing on bursting red and green lights or stars, indicates to an aircraft that it is in or about to enter an active danger, restricted or prohibited area and action must be taken to leave the area immediately (whilst not descending) or change heading to avoid the area.

Bird Strikes. Information on migratory bird movement is given in Notam Class II. A pilot should keep at least 1 500 ft above the surface level over areas where birds are known to concentrate. If a bird strike occurs, it must be reported on the appropriate forms available from the ATC at any licensed aerodrome.

Airmiss procedures

A pilot who thinks he has been endangered by the proximity of another aircraft may file an airmiss report. If radio is carried, it can be filed at once; if it can't be filed in the air, then it is done on landing. Addressed to ATCC, or to any controller or air traffic unit, the standard form is:

(a) THIS IS AIRMISS REPORT
(b) Callsign

(c) Position of Airmiss
(d) Heading
(e) Flt level/Altitude
(f) Altimeter setting
(g) Aircraft attitude
(h) Weather conditions
(i) Date, time
(j) Description of the other aircraft
(k) First sighting distance and details of flight paths of the two aircraft
(l) Estimated minimum horizontal and vertical distances between aircraft involved.

If the first stop is abroad, it can still be filed; AFTN will dispatch it.
The initial report must be followed within 7 days by completing CA Form
1094, or nothing will come of the complaint. Consequently, the pilot will
be kept informed of any action; he may have to give evidence, and he'll
be told the result of any enquiry.

Low level flying rules

These are pretty strict, and there is a portion of the populace who continually report low flying aircraft, always exaggerating the lowness thereof.
The rules are designed to protect built-up areas, assemblies of people,
and the individual person, vessel, structure, vehicle, his ox and his ass.

Towns, cities and settlements are protected by the rule that, if you are
on a notified route, or obeying ATC instructions on special VFR, you must
fly at such a height that in the event of failure of the power unit, you
can clear the area without danger to life or property on the surface. On
any other flight, the lowest height is either:

(a) 1 500 ft above the highest fixed object within 2 000 ft of the aircraft,
or
(b) sufficient height to clear the area safely, without causing danger
to persons or property on the surface, should you get an engine
failure.

And of these two, you have no choice but to fly at the higher.

A helicopter cannot fly below that height which would enable it to
alight without danger to persons or property on the surface in the event
of a failure of the power unit. The CAA may give permission for flight
below 1 500 ft above the highest object within 2 000 ft of the helicopter,
however, and also permit flight over certain areas at gliding height.

Assembly of persons. Unless you are a police aircraft, or taking part
in a flying display, you cannot fly over or within 3 000 ft of any open
air assembly of more than 1 000 persons, except with the written permission of the CAA and the written consent of the organisers, and then not
below such height as would enable it to alight clear of the assembly in
the event of failure of the power unit. It is very distracting to batsmen,

too. Should you break the rules it is a recognised defence to show that the flight was made at a reasonable height and that you were not connected with the assembly in any way.

Persons, vessels, vehicles and structures. The general rule is that an aircraft may not fly closer than 500 ft to any person, vessel, vehicle or structure. The following are the exceptions from the general rule:

(a) an aircraft taking-off or landing
(b) a glider hill-soaring
(c) when taking part in an aircraft display and flying over an assembly of persons
(d) a police aircraft
(e) an aircraft engaged in dropping articles or training for such operation, as allowed under the ANO
(f) an aircraft flying in accordance with the terms of aerial application certificate (agriculture, horticulture, forestry work).

Meteorology

Much of this has been covered in the Met section of this book, but we shall run over the material specifically laid down in the Law syllabus, and the result can only be for the best.

The Organisation of Met services to aviation in the UK is as follows:

Main Offices are located at ATCCs and major aerodromes, always open, and they supply met information and forecasts to their own aerodromes and observing offices attached to them. Charts are prepared every three hours, and oftener if required. They control and advise subsidiary and observing offices.

Subsidiary Offices are located at civil airfields of intermediate importance, open to suit local requirements. They issue forecasts and other met information.

An **Observing Office** is located at a minor aerodrome; it stays open for 24 hours if it is a synoptic reporting station, otherwise it is open to suit local requirements. It issues weather reports, but not forecasts, but it always has the facilities of its main or subsidiary office at its disposal.

The Meteorological Watch Office is the name given to the main office at the ATCC; it keeps a continuous watch over the weather in its area, advises ATC on diversions, liaises with other Met offices in the area, provides en route Met forecasts, and initiates SIGMET messages, which are warnings to aircraft in flight of dangerous weather occurring or likely to occur.

Pre-flight procedures:

(1) Give notice of intended flight at least 4 hours prior to a flight of 500 nm or more; 2 hours notice is sufficient for shorter flights.

(2) On receipt of the notice, the met office collects all the relevant information and prepares the forecast.

(3) The documents are handed over in the met office, where telephone briefing is given if personal appearance is not possible.

(4) Forecasts for destination and alternate airfields are included in the document, prepared by the aerodromes concerned, not the departure field. If this is not possible, the departure aerodrome will produce the forecasts and state their origin.

Regular broadcasts of met information are made by London and Preston ATCC on a continuous basis on VHF frequencies in plain language. They are called Volmet broadcasts, and cover weather for selected aerodromes in the shape of reports with expected trend added if the forecaster is on duty. Each cycle is preceded by a time, this being the time of the observations; a report is broadcast for 30 minutes after this time, and for a further 30 minutes if no fresh report has come in. After that, 'no report received' is broadcast. The contents of the broadcast are standard: surface W/V, visibility, RVR, weather, cloud, temperature, dew point and QNH, in that order. Trend forecasts may be issued as noted above, except of course for RVR which is never forecast. CAVOK is given if visibility is 10 km or more **and** there's no cloud below 5 000 ft, or below the highest sector altitude,. whichever is greater, and no cumulo-nimbus, **and** there is no precipitation or thunderstorms, fog or low drifting snow. When TREND is given, it is a forecast for the next two hours, and the following terms are used:

TREND	trend forecast
GRADU	gradual change at a constant rate
RAPID	rapid change (in $\frac{1}{2}$ hour or less)
INTER	intermittent change, conditions fluctuating
TEMPO	change expected to last less than one hour
NOSIG	no significant change expected
PROB	percentage probability

It was all valuable revision, anyway, with a few new points.

Automatic Terminal Information Service (ATIS). ATIS broadcast services operate at a number of aerodromes. They contain an abridged version of VOL-MET broadcasts in the form of arrival and departure messages and are broadcast either on an RT frequency or on VOR transmissions.

Search and Rescue

Responsibility for search and rescue in the UK rests with the joint civil/ Service organisations. The country is divided into two search and rescue regions, each having a central headquarters called the Rescue Co-ordination Centre (RCC). These are located at Edinburgh and Plymouth, and are authorised to call out various public bodies for S & R duties. The RAF provides the primary airborne force for these duties. Other elements are the RAF Mountain Rescue Units, the RNLI, Coastguards, Police, ocean weather ships. RN helicopters and ships together with civilian aircraft, merchant ships and military personnel make up the secondary force.

Distress is when an aircraft is in grave and imminent danger and requires immediate assistance. The pilot sends any of the following signals:
  (a) by R/T: the spoken word 'MAYDAY'
  (b) by visual signal:
     (i) SOS (...−−−...)
     (ii) a succession of pyro lights, fired at short intervals, each showing a single red light
     (iii) a parachute flare showing a red light
  (c) by sound signals other than R/T:
     (i) SOS
     (ii) a continuous sounding with any sound apparatus.

Difficulty (or Safety). This means the pilot is in difficulty enough to compel him to land but he does not require immediate assistance. The signals are:

  (a) a succession of white pyro lights
  (b) repeated switching on and off of the landing lights
  (c) repeated switching on and off of the navigation lights at irregular intervals.

Urgency. The pilot has an urgent message to transmit concerning the safety of a ship, aircraft, vehicle or other property, or of a person on board or within sight of the aircraft. The signals are:
  (a) by R/T, the spoken word 'PAN'
  (b) by visual signal XXX (−..−−..−−..−)
  (c) by sound signals other than R/T, the signal XXX.

After a ditching or crash landing, full use should be made of equipment on board the aircraft to draw the attention of search aircraft. Survivors in a dinghy may use:
  (a) distress flares and cartridges
  (b) heliograph
  (c) dinghy radio
  (d) whistle (to draw attention of surface search craft)
  (e) fluorescent dye marker
  (f) fly a flag with a ball above or below it; this is an international distress signal.
Survivors of a crash landing in isolated areas should use to attract attention when search aircraft or surface craft are seen or heard:
  (a) distress flares and cartridges
  (b) heliograph
  (c) dinghy radio

    (d) ground-air signals
    (e) flashing light
    (f) triangular fire or smoke.
The ground-air signals mentioned in (d) above are internationally recognised and are in line with the Code of Signals used by mariners.

Make the symbols as large as possible with materials which contrast with the background:

(i) Need assistance	V
(ii) Need medical help	X
(iii) Proceeding in this direction	→
(iv) Yes	Y
(v) No	N

An aircraft observing you in distress will keep you in sight, fix the position, report to ATCC, act on ATCC instructions and take charge over arriving aircraft.

And just in case you might think all this is conjured up to exaggerate an unlikely occurrence in the over-populated UK, a private aircraft in the fine summer of 1971 was reported missing on a 100 nm trip to the Isle of Wight and was not found for two months – in Hampshire.

Facilitation

We deal here with the rules and regulations about Customs, airport formalities and health insofar as they affect private pilots on trips in and out of the UK.

Arrival in the UK from abroad of a private flight, i.e. a non-scheduled non-commercial flight must make its first landing at a Customs aerodrome. What constitutes a Customs aerodrome is defined shortly. An aircraft may cross the UK coast anywhere that does not contravene any of the rules of flight such as danger area, controlled airspace.

Departure to foreign climes (and Channel Islands, Isle of Man, and Northern Ireland come into this category) must similarly be made from Customs airfields. Once cleared, it cannot land again in the UK before departure abroad, unless by reason of force majeure, except at the Customs airport named in the General Declaration.

Documents. One copy of the General Declaration is required for Customs, but this is dispensed with if no fare paying passengers or goods are carried. A Carnet de Passages en Douanes or Customs Form C 42 in duplicate is required, on which the pilot undertakes to return the aircraft to the UK within one month; the duplicate must be retained and presented to Customs on return.

Technical stops are generally unrestricted provided they are made for non-traffic purposes.

Passengers. An alien is required to produce a landing card, embarkation card, valid passport and with certain exceptions a visa. And if you bring into the UK a Commonwealth citizen who proposes to seek employment here, he must have a Dept. of Employment permit. A passport is not required in respect of certain European countries provided the person holds a national identity card together with a Visitor's card issued by travel agencies or airlines. A passenger in transit is not required to produce documents. Commonwealth citizens require a passport and are subject to the Immigration Act. The following are exempt from the Act:

(a) those born in the UK
(b) the holder of a passport issued by the British Passport Office
(c) a citizen of UK and Colonies whose passport has been issued by the British High Commission and is not endorsed 'issued on behalf of the Colony'.

Health. Any person entering the UK may be examined medically if suspected of suffering from infectious disease. Any person leaving the UK may be examined if suspected of suffering from a quarantinable disease. The international certificate of smallpox vaccination is necessary in the case of persons entering the UK from certain countries. People who do not have such a certificate may be offered vaccination and may be put under surveillance or in isolation.

Customs aerodromes are categorised as follows: A, Customs officers are in attendance at all times; B, during normal working hours on weekdays, except public holidays; C, by prior notice only.

Customs requirements for private flights are in the main those demanded of the private citizen coming in or going out. If a forced landing is made after clearance on departure though, the pilot must, if he's lobbed down where there's no Customs, inform Customs or police, produce documents on demand, and ensure that no person or goods leave the immediate vicinity of the aircraft without consent of Customs, except for reasons of health, safety or preservation of life,

The Air Navigation Order 1985
We only include a resumé of those Articles which apply to the Private Pilot's Licence; numbering of Articles and paragraphs need not be memorised.

Registration of Aircraft – Articles 3,4, Schedule 1. Apart from a few special exceptions (given in Art. 3) an aircraft may not be flown over the UK unless it is registered, either in the UK or abroad, and it is displaying its registration markings. If a private pilot is an owner or a part-owner in a syndicate, he is responsible for informing the CAA if any particular is changed from those given when the aircraft was registered.

Certificate of Airworthiness – Articles 7,8, Schedules 2,3. An aircraft may not be flown unless it has a valid Certificate of Airworthiness (C of A), although as with the Certificate of Registration the ANO does allow a few special exceptions. Sometimes an aircraft can be issued a 'Permit to Fly'. The pilot must comply with any conditions laid down in the

C of A or Permit. The C of A specifies the category into which the aircraft is placed and it can only be flown for that specified purpose. The categories are:

(a) Transport Category (Passenger): Any purpose.
(b) Transport Category (Cargo): Any purpose, other than public transport of passengers.
(c) Aerial Work Category: Any purpose other than public transport.
(d) Private Category: Any purpose other than public transport or aerial work.
(e) Special Category: Any purpose, other than public transport, specified in the C of A but excluding the carriage of passengers unless expressly permitted.

Certificate of Maintenance Review, Technical Log, Repairs – Articles 9,10.11. An aircraft in Transport or Aerial Work Categories in its C of A must be maintained, with its equipment, to a CAA-approved Maintenance Schedule and have a valid Certificate of Maintenance Review. A Technical Log has to be kept in which the aircraft commander must enter:

(a) times of take-off and landing
(b) details of any defects in the aircraft and its equipment or a positive statement 'No Defects'
(c) any other details called for by the CAA.

Except in the few special cases given in the ANO, if the aircraft or its equipment has to be overhauled, repaired, replaced, modified or maintained then a Certificate of Release to Service must be issued on the completion of the work. Some specific minor repairs or replacements may be carried out by the pilot.

Aircraft equipment – Articles 13,14, Schedules 5,6.
Standards are laid down as to minimum equipment that must be carried for particular flights. The equipment has to be of approved types and installed and maintained in a laid down manner. Schedule 6 gives the radio and radio navigation equipment to be carried while Schedule 5 specifies all the other equipment. The Schedules cover all flight circumstances and comprehensive scales of equipment, all of which are listed in the syllabus. Learn first the scale of equipment applicable to your own aircraft operation.

Aircraft, engine, propeller log-books – Article 15. For an aircraft not exceeding 2 730 kg maximum total weight authorised, an operator must keep a separate logbook for the aircraft, for each of its engines and for each propeller fitted to it. Entries must be laid out as Schedule 7 of the ANO as soon as possible and certainly within 7 days of the expiry of the Certificate of Maintenance Review. Logbooks have to be preserved for two years after the aircraft, engine or propeller has been taken out of use or destroyed.

Aircraft Weight Schedule – Article 16. Also dealt with later in chapter 13. All gliders and flying machines with a C of A must be weighed and have their Centre of Gravity (CG) determined. After weighing, the aircraft operator must prepare a weight schedule which gives either the basic weight (i.e. empty aircraft + unusable fuel and oil + specified equipment) or another datum weight approved for that aircraft by CAA, together with the CG position for either the aircraft at its basic weight or as approved by CAA. The weight schedule has to be preserved for 6 months after the aircraft is reweighed for a new weight schedule.

Aircraft Crew Composition – Article 18. Simply says 'An aircraft shall not fly unless it carries a flight crew of the number and description required by the country in which it is registered.' In the UK, the simplest case must be: Minimum Crew = 1 = The Pilot!

Licences, Ratings – Article 19, Schedule 9. This specifies that a person must be at least 17 years of age before holding a PPL. After passing the PPL examinations and signing the licence, the licence holder is required to meet various other requirements to keep the licence going e.g. periodical tests and medical examinations. There is no maximum period of validity for the licence but medical fitness certificates' validity become shorter with increase of age over 40 years. Schedule 9 also defines what is meant by 'Solo' and 'Cross-country' flights as follows:

'Solo flight' means a flight on which the pilot of the aircraft is not accompanied by a person holding a pilot's licence granted or rendered valid under this Order. i.e. The ANO.

'Cross-country flight' means any flight during the course of which the aircraft is more than 3 nautical miles from the aerodrome of departure.

As for the privileges, the holder of a PPL is entitled to fly as pilot in command, but note the following limitations.

(a) He may fly as pilot in command only those types of aircraft included in his licences.

(b) He is not permitted to fly for the purpose of public transport or aerial work. 'Aerial work' is a flight for any purpose other than public transport, in respect of which hire or reward is given or promised. The club instructors using club aircraft and training club members and private instructors using their own aircraft are the only exceptions to this limitation.

(c) Until he gets an IMC rating –
    (i) When on a flight outside controlled airspace he may not fly as pilot in command when the flight visibility is less than $1\frac{1}{2}$ nm.

(ii) On a flight still outside controlled airspace but now carrying a passenger, he may not fly

above 3 000 ft	*at 3 000 ft and below*
in IMC	*when visibility is less*
	than 3 nm

(iii) In a control zone when on a special VFR he may not fly in flight visibility of less than five nm except on a route or an aerodrome traffic zone notified for the purpose. With the IMC rating he may fly in flight visibility of less than 5 nm but not less than $1\frac{1}{2}$ nm.

(iv) On a flight at night when a passenger is carried he must hold a night rating AND either an instrument rating or be able to show that he has, within the immediately preceding 6 months, carried out as pilot in command not less than 5 take-offs and 5 landings at night.

Personal Flying Log Books – Article 22. A personal flying log book must be kept by every member of a flight crew, and by every person who flies for the purpose of qualifying for the initial grant or renewal of a licence, or taking a test or receiving instruction. The following particulars are recorded:

Name and address of the holder

Particulars of holder's licence

Name and address of employer, if any.

Particulars of all flights made as a member of a flight crew, including:

   (i) date, time, duration and places of arrival and departure of each flight

  (ii) type and registration marks of the aircraft

 (iii) the capacity in which the holder acted

 (iv) particulars of any special conditions under which the flight was conducted, including night flying and instrument flying

  (v) particulars of any test or examination undertaken whilst in flight.

As we shall see when dealing with offences in relation to documents – Article 63 – all logbook entries must be made in ink or in indelible pencil. Your logbook is and will be a treasured document. Do take care with the entries.

Instruction in Flying – Article 23. Flying instruction may not be given unless the instructor has a valid licence entitling him to act as Pilot-in-Command for the purpose and in the circumstances of the instruction, together with either a flying instructor's or assistant flying instructor's rating.

Pre-flight action by Commander of aircraft – Article 32. This article applies to the commander of UK registered aircraft only.

(i) Ensure that the flight may safely be made, taking into account the weather reports and forecasts for the route and aerodromes likely to be used, and alternative action if the flight does not go to plan

(ii) Check all aircraft equipment is serviceable

(iii) Check that the aircraft is in every way fit for flight

(iv) Check that certificate of maintenance is valid, and will stay valid for period of the trip

(v) Check load for security, distribution and weight

(vi) Ensure sufficient fuel, oil and engine coolant is carried for the flight plus adequate contingency reserve

(vii) In the case of a balloon that sufficient ballast is carried

(viii) In the case of a flying machine, check that the aircraft can safely take off, reach and maintain a safe height, and make a safe landing, with regard to the performance of the aircraft

(ix) That all pre-flight checks have been carried out.

Pilots to remain at controls – Article 33. The commander of a UK-registered flying machine or glider has to ensure that:

(i) one pilot is at the controls at all times in flight,

(ii) if the aircraft is required to carry 2 pilots then both pilots are at the controls during take-off and landing,

(iii) each pilot at the controls wears a seat belt or harness,

(iv) if it is so required under the ANO, a harness must be worn during take-off and landing.

Operation of Radio – Article 35. In flight, whoever is operating the radio must:

(i) have a valid RT licence,

(ii) only operate approved and licensed equipment,

(iii) operate the radio equipment in accordance with the conditions of the licence,

(iv) operate as notified or in accordance with ATC instructions,

(v) keep a telecommunication logbook if RT communication is not with a radio station on land or a ship which provides a radio service for aircraft.

Flight Recording – Article 37. Aeroplanes over 5 700 kg and helicopters over 2 700 kg maximum total weight authorised, in certain circumstances, are required to carry and operate flight recording systems from the beginning of the take-off run to the end of the landing run. The operator has to preserve the records:

(i) of the last 25 hours of recording made,

(ii) of a representative flight made in the last 12 months, together with the details of that flight,

(iii) of (i) and (ii) for as long as CAA require.

Towing Gliders – Article 38. An aircraft can only tow a glider if its C of A permits it. The combined length in flight of towing aircraft, tow rope and glider must not exceed 150 metres. Before take-off the commander of the tug-aircraft is responsible for safety checks including the strength and good condition of the tow rope, the intended flight path, signals to be used. The Article also requires that the glider must be attached to the tug aircraft by the tow rope before the aircraft takes off.

Towing, Picking up and Raising – Article 39. Unless its C of A permits, an aircraft cannot be used to tow, pick up or raise anything. Launching or picking up of tow ropes, banners or suchlike is only allowed at aerodromes. Towing (except a glider) may not be carried out at night or in a flight visibility of less than 1 nm. A helicopter when flying with an article, person or animal suspended beneath it cannot carry a passenger unless he/she is performing duties relating to the suspended load, nor can the helicopter fly over a congested area of a city, town or settlement.

Dropping of Articles and Animals – Article 40. Articles and animals are not to be dropped or permitted to be dropped from an aircraft in flight where such drop would endanger persons or property. Over the UK articles and animals are not allowed to be dropped (irrespective of whether attached to a parachute or not) from an aircraft in flight. However, articles may be dropped with the commander's authority in any of the following circumstances:

(a) for the purpose of saving life;
(b) the jettisoning of fuel or other articles in case of emergency;
(c) dropping of ballast in the form of fine sand or water;
(d) the dropping of articles solely for the purpose of navigating the aircraft;
(e) the dropping of ropes, banners or similar articles towed by an aircraft at an aerodrome in accordance with prescribed regulations;
(f) the dropping of articles for the purpose of agriculture, horticulture. forestry, public health etc.
(g) the dropping of wind indicators, with CAA permission, to enable parachute descents to be made.

For the purpose of this article the meaning of the word 'dropping' is extended to include 'projecting' and 'lowering'.

A helicopter may lower a person, animal or an article if its certificate of airworthiness contains an express provision that it may be used for that purpose.

Dropping Persons – Article 41. Over the UK, a person may not drop, be dropped, permitted to be dropped or jump from an aircraft except under and in accordance with the terms of a written permission from CAA. Dropping includes projecting and lowering and must not endanger persons or property. The C of A of the aircraft has to include express provision for its use for parachuting, and the aircraft must be operated in accordance with the parachute manual. The permission-holder has to ensure his parachute manual is available to the CAA, every employee and every person engaged in his parachuting activities.

Carriage of Weapons and Munitions of War – Article 43. Munitions of war means such weapons and ammunition, explosives or noxious substances or parts thereof as are designed for use in warfare. It is unlawful to carry, or cause to be carried, such articles in an aircraft.

It is now unlawful for a person to carry or have in his charge any weapon while on board any UK registered aircraft. A weapon, not meant for use in warfare, may be carried in an inaccessible part of the aircraft provided it is not loaded. Weapons may be carried on board an aircraft registered elsewhere than in the UK if such carriage is lawful in the country of registration and they are carried for the safety of the aircraft or the passengers (This proviso legalises the carriage of the so-called 'security marshal').

Carriage of dangerous goods – Article 44. Dangerous goods may be carried on or underslung below an aircraft under regulations made by the Secretary of State which state:

(a) certain articles and substances are classified as dangerous goods;
(b) which categories of dangerous goods aircraft may not carry;
(c) conditions of packing, marking, labelling, handling, loading and documentation of dangerous goods;
(d) who must be informed of the carriage of dangerous goods;
(e) the documents that can be required to be produced to the CAA.

In the same way as commercial airlines draw passengers' attention to potentially dangerous items that they cannot carry in their baggage, so private pilots should always check what might be unwittingly carried in their aircraft.

Method of carriage of persons – Article 45. A person shall only be carried in proper accommodation of an aircraft and will not be towed in anything other than a glider or a flying machine. A person may have temporary access to:

(a) any part of the aircraft in the interests of its safety or of any person or thing on board;
(b) that part of the aircraft designed to have an access in a cargo aircraft.

Imperilling safety of aircraft – Article 47. A person shall not recklessly or negligently act in a manner likely to endanger an aircraft or any person therein.

Imperilling safety of person or property – Article 48. A person shall not recklessly or negligently cause or permit an aircraft to endanger any person or property. It's worth reading these two again, as the legalese may bemuse you to lose the message.

Drunkenness in aircraft – Article 49.
(i) a person shall not enter any aircraft when drunk, or be drunk on an aircraft
(ii) as for any members of the crew, the limit of drinking or drug taking is any extent which will impair his capacity to act as his duties demand.

Smoking in aircraft – Article 50. When the 'No Smoking' sign is on, it must be obeyed; the notice must be visible to every passenger. This is the rule: smoking is not legally prohibited on take-off and landing, only when the sign is on.

Authority of Aircraft Commander – Article 51. Everyone on a UK-registered aircraft must obey all lawful orders given by the Commander for the purpose of safety of the aircraft and of persons and property carried, or for the safety, efficiency or regularity of air navigation.

Documents to be carried – Article 57 and Schedule 12. If a flight is over the UK only and begins and ends at the same aerodrome, no documents need to be carried. When on a flight abroad in an UK registered aircraft, for a purpose other than public transport or aerial work, the following docs must be carried:

(i) Certificate of Airworthiness
(ii) Certificate of Registration
(iii) Radio licence of the aircraft and the Telecommunication log book
(iv) Crew licences.

Production of documents – Article 59. The commander of an aircraft must produce all documents required to be carried under Article 57 and Schedule 12 above when requested within reasonable time; that time will be dependent on circumstances, for who can define 'reasonable'? A personal flying log book must similarly be presented on request to a properly authorised person.

A holder of a licence must produce it to an authorised person within 5 days, if it was not required to be carried on the aircraft.

And your personal flying log book can be called for by an authorised person up to two years after the last entry.

Offences in relation to Documents and Records – Article 63.
1. A person shall not with intent to deceive:
    (a) Use any licence, certificate, approval, permission, exemption or other document which has been forged, revoked, suspended or to which he is not entitled.

(b) Lend any licence, certificate, approval, exemption, etc., to any other person, or

(c) Procure any licence, etc., for himself or any other person by false representation.

Any reference in this paragraph to licence, approval, etc., includes a copy or purported copy thereof.

2. A person shall not mutilate, alter or render illegible any log book or other document required under this order, or help any other to do so, or make a false entry or commit a material omission or destroy any such document.

3. All entries in a log book or record are to be in ink or indelible pencil.

4. A person shall not knowingly make in a load sheet an incorrect entry in a material particular, or any material omission.

Rules of the Air and Air Traffic Control – Article 64. The Rules of the Air and Air Traffic Control Regulations, published as a separate Statutory Instrument, are binding, with one minor exception, on:

(a) all aircraft within the UK; and

(b) all aircraft registered in the UK, wherever they may be. It is an offence to contravene, to permit the contravention of, or to fail to comply with the Rules of the Air and Air Traffic Control except:

(a) when avoiding immediate danger, or

(b) when complying with the law of the country the aircraft is in, or

(c) when complying with Military Flying Regs or Flying Orders issued by the Secretary of State in relation to an aircraft of which the commander is acting as such in the course of his duties as a member of H.M. Forces.

If the contravention was made to avoid immediate danger, the pilot must report the matter within 10 days of the incident as follows:

(a) to the competent authority of the country in whose territory the incident occurred;

(b) to the CAA if it occurred over the high seas. No provision in the Rules of the Air and ATC exonerates a person from the consequences of:

(a) neglect in the use of lights or signals;

(b) neglect of normal precautions, in all circumstances.

Power to Prohibit or Restrict Flying – Article 69.

1. The Secretary of State may restrict or prohibit flying over certain areas in the following circumstances:

(a) when there is a large gathering of people;

(b) in the vicinity of an aircraft race, exhibition of flying or contest;

(c) for reasons of national defence or reasons affecting public interests.

The prohibition may apply generally to all aircraft, or to particular types or class.

2. If an aircraft contravenes the prohibition under 1c, the commander must take the action already described earlier in this chapter under Airspace Restrictions on page 159.

Balloons and Airships – Article 70. Within the UK, without CAA's written permission,

1. a captive balloon or kite may not be flown more than 60 metres above ground level or within 60 metres of any vessel, vehicle or structure, nor within 5 km of an aerodrome;

2. a balloon, either captive or free, which exceeds 2 metres in any linear dimension (including any basket or equipment attached) may not be flown in controlled airspace;

3. an airship may not be moored.

Use of Aerodromes for Public Transport or Flying Instruction – Article 71. A public transport aircraft carrying passengers, or an aircraft on instruction in flying is prohibited from taking off or landing except at:

1. either a Government aerodrome or a CAA-owned or managed aerodrome which is notified as available for such take-off and landing, or where permission has been obtained; or

2. an aerodrome licensed for the purpose.

If the maximum total weight authorised of an aircraft is 2 730 kg or less, the prohibition applies only if

(a) the aircraft is on a scheduled journey for the purpose of public transport of passengers or on a flight for the purpose of flying training, or

(b) the flight is for the purpose of transport of passengers and begins and ends at the same aerodrome, or

(c) the flight is for the purpose of public transport of passengers at night.

The prohibition also applies to helicopters and gyroplanes engaged on such flights as are given in (a) above. Lastly, it applies to gliders which are flying for the purpose of the public transport of passengers or for the purpose of instruction in flying. It does not apply to gliders being flown under arrangements made by a flying club and carrying no person other than a member of the club.

Aviation Fuel – Article 82. This Article defines 'aviation fuel' as meaning 'fuel intended for use in aircraft'. It also lays down that no-one may cause or permit any fuel to be used in an aircraft if he knows (or has reason to believe) that it is unfit for that purpose.

Penalties – Article 90. This Article specifies the maximum penalties to which pilots may be liable if convicted for contravention of the ANO or the Regulations made under it. The penalties vary from a fine of £400 on summary conviction for some offences to a £2 000 fine and/or up to 2 years imprisonment for offences such as making false reports or use of unfit 'aviation' fuel.

Interpretation – Article 96. This is the part of the ANO which gives a Glossary of Definitions. On a re-read of this chapter, use it to check you really know the definition of each term used from 'aerial work' onwards through 'night' to 'runway visual range'.

Privileges of Licences and Ratings – Schedule 9. Apart from the privileges already mentioned on page 167, the following are also in the PPL syllabus:

PPL (Helicopters & Gyroplanes). The licence-holder may fly as Pilot-in-Command (PIC) or co-pilot of any type specified in the aircraft rating included in the licence provided that when flying at night as PIC on a flight on which a passenger is carried or instruction is given in flying, a night rating is held and:

(a) 5 night take-offs and 5 night landings have been made as PIC in the last 90 days; and

(b) an Instrument Rating held or, as an alternative to the IR, 5 night flights have been made as PIC each consisting of a take-off, transition from hover to forward flight, a climb to at least 500 ft and a landing.

PPL (Balloons & Airships). Again the pilot must have the balloon or airship type rating in his licence. In the previous 13 months, a licence-holder must have satisfactorily completed a flight test or made 5 flights as PIC.

Ratings: The ratings that can be added to a PPL comprise:

(a) Aircraft – A valid certificate of test or experience must be held for the appropriate group and maximum total weight authorised (MTWA).

Group A – Single engine aeroplanes not over 5 700 kg MTWA.

Group B – Multi engine aeroplanes not over 5 700 kg MTWA.

Group C – Aeroplanes MTWA exceeding 5 700 kg.

Group D – Microlight aeroplanes.

(b) IMC Rating

(c) Instrument Rating (Aeroplanes) or (Helicopters)

(d) Night Rating (Aeroplanes) or (Helicopters and Gyroplanes)

(e) Towing Rating (Flying Machines)

(f) Flying Instructor Rating

(g) Assistant Flying Instructor Rating.

Certificate of Test or Experience – Schedule 9. The Schedule details the nature of the tests. A Certificate of Test is valid for 13 months forward from the date of the test. A Certificate of Experience relates to the period of 13 months prior to its signing and is also valid for 13 months from the date that it is signed. Holders of Certificates are responsible for ensuring renewal within the period of validity to keep the privilege.

Rules of the Air

The following rules for avoiding collisions, both in the air and on the ground, are prescribed in the Rules of the Air and Air Traffic Control Regulations, 1985, but notwithstanding that a flight is made with air traffic control clearance, it is the duty of the commander of an aircraft to ensure that his aircraft does not collide with another aircraft. You may construe that piece of verbiage as 'if you've got the death wish, keep your head in the cockpit'.

An aircraft is prohibited from flying in such proximity to other aircraft as to create a danger of collision.

An aircraft is not permitted to formate with other aircraft unless the commanders have agreed to do so.

For the purposes of this rule, a glider and a flying machine which is towing it is considered to be a single aircraft, under the command of the commander of the flying machine.

Under the rules to follow, one aircraft may have the right of way; the other may be obliged to give way. The one which has the right of way shall maintain its heading and speed. The one which has to give way shall avoid passing over or under the other aircraft, or crossing it, unless passing well clear of it.

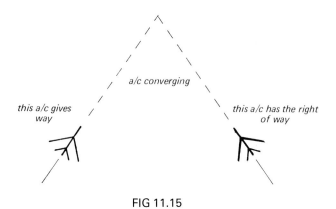

FIG 11.15

Rules for two aircraft in flight

1. Two aircraft converging. In this case, if the aircraft are of a different class, the order of precedence applies, which is:

First: balloons
Second: gliders
Third: airships
Fourth: flying machines

But where the two aircraft are of the same class, e.g. flying machines, then the aircraft which has the other on its right shall give way. Fig. 11.15 illustrates. Powered aircraft must give way to other aircraft which are towing e.g. a banner.

2. Two aircraft approaching head-on. Each alters heading to the right.

3. Overtaking. Aircraft which is being overtaken in the air has the right of way. An overtaking aircraft, whether climbing, descending or in level flight, has the duty to keep out of the way of the other by altering heading to the right. It will continue to keep clear of the other until the other aircraft is passed and is clear, notwithstanding any change in the relative position of the two.

A glider overtaking another glider in the UK may alter its heading to right or left.

Access and movement on aerodromes. A person or vehicle may not go on any part of an active aerodrome without permission of the person in charge and subject to his conditions. Similarly conditions of access to the manoeuvring area of an aerodrome apply if there is an ATC, when the ATCO's permission is required. An aircraft may not taxy on the apron or manoeuvring area without similar authorisation.

Rules of way on the ground

1. Between aircraft and vehicles, the order of precedence is:
   First: taking off and landing aircraft
   Second: vehicles towing aircraft
   Third: aircraft
   Fourth: vehicles
2. Subject to the above,
   (i) when two flying machines on the ground are approaching head-on, each shall alter heading to the right
   (ii) when two flying machines are on converging courses, the one which has the other on its right shall give way, and avoid crossing ahead of the other unless passing well clear of it
   (iii) a flying machine which is being overtaken has the right of way, and the overtaking flying machine shall keep out of the other's way by altering its heading to the **left** until it has passed the other and is clear, notwithstanding any change in the relative positions of the two flying machines.

Are you still there in your flying machine?

Right-hand traffic rule. An aircraft flying in the UK within sight of the ground and following a road, railway or some similar landmark, is to keep such a landmark on its left.

Aerobatic Manoeuvres. These are not permitted over the congested area of any town, city or settlement, or within controlled airspace, although the appropriate ATC may give permission for aerobatics in controlled airspace.

Picking up and dropping tow-ropes. We have seen that Article 39 limits these activities to aerodromes. Rule 34 specifies that these activities must also only be in accordance with arrangements made with ATC or whoever is in charge of the aerodrome, in the designated and marked area, and with aircraft 'flying in the direction appropriate for landing'.

General Rules
Knocking around here in the official document under consideration are sundry other rules of the air distinct from how and where to fly.

Weather reports and forecasts
1. Before flight, the pilot shall examine all the weather reports and forecasts for his proposed route in order to determine whether IMC prevail or are likely to.

2. An aircraft which cannot communicate by radio with the ATC at destination airfield shall not begin a flight to an aerodrome within a control zone if the weather on arrival is likely to have ground visibility of less than 5 nm or cloud ceiling of less than 1 500 ft – unless permission is given before hand by the destination ATC, of course.

Notification of Arrival. Briefly, if a pilot leaves or enters the UK on a flight for which a flight plan is filed, he should, on arrival at the destination field, do all he can to let the departure aerodrome know he's arrived. And if the authorities concerned have been warned to expect his arrival, the commander of the aircraft must let them know soonest of any change in planned destination and any likely delay in arrival of 45 minutes or more.

This rule also specifies that the commander of an aircraft of over 5 700 kg MTWA flying in the UK to a destination more than 40 kilometres away must file a Flight Plan for search and rescue purposes.

Display of lights by aircraft
This section is not as dull as it sounds, though truly there are a number of details to be committed to memory. For what it's worth, we must tell you that the topic gave a didactic element to the doodles of aeroplanes that our students were forever drawing.

Over the UK at night, all aircraft without exception must comply with the rules that follow for the display of lights. We have coined the term 'basic lights', and these are (Fig. 11.16).
   (i) A green light of at least five candela showing to the starboard side through an angle of 110° from dead ahead in the horizontal plane.
   (ii) A red light of at least 5 candela showing to the port side through an angle of 110° from dead ahead in the horizontal plane.
   (iii) A white light of at least 3 candela showing through angles of 70° from dead astern to each side in the horizontal plane.
An 'anti-collision light, in respect of rotorcraft is a flashing red showing in **all** directions. In respect of all other aircraft, it may be either a flashing red light or a flashing white light (of 400 candela in future).

FIG 11.16 Plan view

FIG 11.17   Elevation

On the ground

1. **Stationary** flying machines on the apron or in the maintenance area need show no lights whatever.

2. **Moving** flying machines on any part of an aerodrome must show:
   (a) all lights which would be on in flight, **or**
   (b) three basic lights flashing
   (c) three basic lights, all steady.

In the air

1. Flying machines registered in the UK having a maximum total author-ised weight of more than 5 700 kg (12 500 lb) must show:
   (a) basic lights, steady and
   (b) anti-collision light.

2. Flying machines registered in the UK having a maximum total author-ised weight of 5 700 kg (12 500 lb) and less must show:

    (a) basic lights, steady **or**
    (b) basic lights steady and an anti-collision light, **or**
    (c) basic lights flashing and an additional white light of at least 20 candela showing in all directions. The basic lights flash in alternation with the flashing white. The sequence is mandatory under this set-up, but an anti-collision light may be added at option.
  3. Any other flying machine must display:
    (a) basic lights, steady, **or**
    (b) basic lights steady plus anti-collision light, **or**
    (c) basic lights flashing, with or without anti-collision light, **or**
    (d) basic lights flashing alternating with flashing white as in 2 (c) above, with or without anti-collision light, **or**
    (e) basic lights flashing in alternation with a red light of at least 20 candela installed in the tail and showing through the same angles as the white tail light, with or without anti-collision light, **or**
    (f) basic lights flashing in alternation with both red and white lights, with or without anti-collision light.

No other lights must be displayed which might obscure or impair the visibility of mandatory lights.

Where lights are to be shown through specific angles in the horizontal plane, they should be visible through 90° above and below in the vertical plane. This means that the same light which is visible to an aircraft, say, approaching from the rear, is also visible to it above or below the aircraft. See Fig. 11.17.

In the UK, if a navigation light fails in flight and cannot immediately be replaced or repaired, the aircraft must land as soon as it safely can, unless the appropriate air traffic control unit authorises continuance of the flight.

Free balloons flying at night shall display a steady red light of at least 5 candela showing in all directions suspended from 5 to 10 metres below the basket or the lowest part of the balloon if there is no basket.

Captive balloons and kites, when flying at night at a height over 60 metres have:

1. A group of two steady lights (a white 4 metres above a red) showing in all directions and at least 5 candela. The white is placed between 5 and 10 metres below the basket (or lowest part of the balloon).

2. The above group is repeated every 300 metres along the mooring cable, with the lowest group below the cloud base.

3. On the surface, an equilateral triangle of three flashing lights and sides of approximately 25 metres, enclosing the cable mooring point. The cable does not go vertically upwards and the side of the triangle crossed by the cable has two red lights while the corner away from the cable has the green light.

Gliders flying at night may show any system of lights pertaining to an aircraft or just a steady red of at least 5 candela showing in all directions.

Avoiding collisions. When a light of another aircraft is seen at night and appears to be at one's own level, the risk of collision may exist. The primary rule is:

Estimate the relative bearing of the visible light of the aircraft at short intervals. If it stays **constant**, the risk of collision exists, and prompt action must be taken. The action depends on whether you have right of way, or are obliged to give way. But remember that, even if it's your right of way, if the other aircraft does not take avoiding action, you still have the responsibility of doing all that is possible to avoid a collision. If the relative bearing **increases or decreases,** there is no risk of collision. Just keep a wary eye on the other aircraft until a safe distance off.

The rules for avoiding collisions as already outlined still apply, of course, without reservation; at night, it is the light or lights you see that give a clue to the heading of the other. It is well worth scratching on a piece of paper an aircraft on a definite heading, and surrounding it with others, determining the lights visible from that aircraft and the possibility of collision. One such at least will be asked in the PPL exam, take it from us. Here's a sample or two (Fig. 11.18).

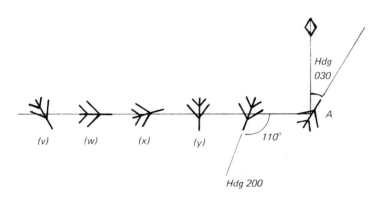

FIG 11.18

From A, another aircraft is visible on a relative bearing of 240, the bearing from the aircraft's nose. The light seen would be as follows.

Aircraft in position (v): red light visible
(w): red and green visible
(x): green light visible
(y): red light visible

aircraft on Hdg 200° would have red light visible, and any change of heading towards 360° would bring its white tail light into A's view.

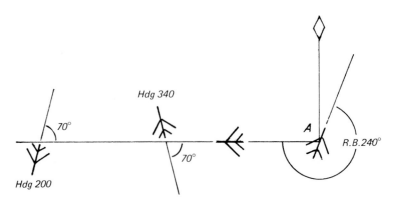

FIG 11.19

In Fig. 11.19, aircraft A, again on Hdg 030°(T), sights another aircraft on a relative bearing of 240° but sees only its white tail light. We see it is on a Hdg 270°, and if it altered Heading by 70° either side of 270°, then the red or green will appear in place of the white once those limits are passed; Hdg 200°(T) and 340°(T) are the limits for the appearance of the white. At (p), Hdg to 199° or less will show the red, at (q), Hdg to 341° or more will show the green.

Marshalling signals

The following are the standard signals made by a marshaller to assist the ground manoeuvres of aircraft. It must be emphasised that the responsibility of avoiding a taxying incident rests with the pilot, who may ignore the signals if he thinks it unwise to comply with them.

Meaning of signal	Description of signal
1. Proceed under guidance of another marshaller	Right or left arm down, the other arm moved across body to point to other marshaller. Fig. 11.20.
2. Move ahead	Arms repeatedly moved upward and backward, beckoning onward. Fig. 11.21.
3. Open up starboard engine or turn to port	Right arm down, left arm repeatedly moved upward and backward. The speed of arm movement indicates the rate of turn. Fig. 11.22.
4. Open up port engine or turn to starboard	Left arm down, the right arm repeatedly moved upward and backward. The speed of arm movement indicates the rate of turn. Fig. 11.23.
5. Stop	Arms repeatedly crossed over the head. The speed of arm movement indicates the urgency of the stop. Fig. 11.24.
6. Start engines	A circular motion of the right hand at head level, with the left arm pointing to the appropriate engine. Fig. 11.25.

FIG 11.20 FIG 11.21 FIG 11.22 FIG 11.23

FIG 11.24   FIG 11.25

FIG 11.26 FIG 11.27 FIG 11.28

FIG 11.29 FIG 11.30 FIG 11.31 FIG 11.32

7. Chocks inserted	Arms extended, the palms facing inward then swung from the extended position inwards. Fig. 11.26.
8. Chocks away	Arms down, the palms facing outwards, then swung outwards. Fig. 11.27.
9. Cut engines	Either arm and hand placed level with the chest, then moved laterally with the palm downward. Fig. 11.28.
10. Slow down	Arms placed down, with the palms towards the ground, then moved up and down several times. Fig. 11.29.
11. Slow down engines on indicated side	Arms placed down with the palms towards the ground, then either the right or left arm moved up and down indicating that the motors on the left or right side as the case may be should be slowed down. Fig. 11.30.
12. This bay	Arms placed above the head in a vertical position. Fig. 11.31.
13. All clear; marshalling finished	Right arm raised at the elbow, with the arm facing forward. Fig. 11.32.

Notification of accidents

Certain accidents become 'reportable' either under Civil Aviation (Investigation of Accidents) Regulations 1983 or Air Navigation (Investigation of Combined Military and Civil Air Accidents) Regulations 1969. Under these two pieces of legislation, accidents under the following circumstances become reportable.

An accident which occurs between the time when any person boards an aircraft with the intention of flight and such time as all persons have disembarked, and in consequence of the accident:

(a) any person suffers death or serious injury while in or upon the aircraft or by direct contact with the aircraft or anything attached thereto or by direct exposure to jet blast; or

(b) the aircraft incurs damage or structural failure, other than

   (i) engine failure or damage, when damage is limited to the engine, its cowling or accessories,

   (ii) damage limited to propellers, wing-tips, antennae, tyres, brakes, fairings, small dents or punctured holes in the aircraft skin, which would adversely affect its structural strength, performance or flight characteristics and would normally require repair or replacement.

(c) the aircraft is missing or completely inaccessible.

What is meant by 'serious injury' is spelt out in the Accident Regulations. Death or serious injury from natural causes, or if self-inflicted or if suffered by a stowaway hiding 'outside areas not normally available in flight to passengers and crew' are not reportable.

The notification is given by the commander of the aircraft or, if he is killed or incapacitated, the operator or any other person on whose behalf he was in command of the aircraft.

The notification is made to the Department of Transport, Accident Investigation Branch, and, if the accident takes place in or over the UK, to the local police authorities in addition.

The quickest means possible are to be used to communicate the notification.

Test questions
A selection of typical test questions on the Law syllabus follows, with answers.

1. A private pilot intending to carry out a flight involving a sea crossing is recommended to submit a flight plan if any part of the flight is more than a certain distance from the coast. This distance is:

(a) 10 miles   (b) 15 miles   (c) 50 miles

2. Outside controlled airspace and above 3 000 ft above mean sea level, a pilot may fly under VFR in the UK, except at night, provided he can remain a minimum distance horizontally and vertically from cloud with a minimum flight visibility distance. These distances are:
(a) 2 000 ft, 500 ft, 3 nm
(b) 2 nm, 1 nm, 4 nm
(c) 1 nm, 1 000 ft, 5 nm

3. At a UK aerodrome, the altimeter check can be carried out:
(a) on the apron
(b) in the flight clearance office
(c) in the flight briefing room

4. Flight Information Regions (FIRs) extend from ground level:
(a) up to but not including FL 245
(b) up to but not including FL 290
(c) with no upper limit

5. The marshalling signal 'arms down, palms facing inward, arms swung from extended position inwards' means:
(a) this bay
(b) turn to port
(c) chocks inserted

6. The Letter 'C' displayed in black against a yellow background indicates:
(a) coffee and refreshments available here
(b) air traffic control unit is situated here
(c) visiting pilots report here

7. The following accident is 'reportable':

(a) your passenger climbing up the aircraft steps, slips and breaks her leg
(b) aircraft on landing bursts a tyre
(c) passenger on the way out to the aircraft slips on the apron and breaks an arm

8. Flying at night, you see the red and green lights of another aircraft, range about 4 nm, and at your altitude or thereabouts, on a relative bearing of 085°
(a) you must give way, as a risk of collision exists
(b) there is a risk of collision, and the other aircraft is on the right and must give way
(c) there is no risk of collision

9. A Customs airport category B, would have Customs attendance:
(a) at all times
(b) during normal working hours
(c) prior notice only

10. When one taxying aircraft wishes to overtake another, it shall alter heading to:
(a) the right
(b) the left
(c) right or left as convenient

11. You take off from an aerodrome which is 500 ft amsl, outside controlled airspace in Wales. On the climb, the altimeter is set to 1013·2 mb at
(a) 2 500 ft above aerodrome level
(b) 3 000 ft above aerodrome level
(c) 3 500 ft above aerodrome level

12. To obtain terrain clearance while on route:
(a) QNE setting is used
(b) QFF setting is used
(c) Regional QNH is used

13. The closest that an aircraft may fly over an assembly of more than 1 000 persons is:
(a) 3 000 ft
(b) 1 000 ft
(c) 1 000 m

14. A private aircraft flying from the UK to Belgium, and not equipped with radio, must carry the following documents:
(a) crew licences only
(b) certificates of registration and airworthiness and crew licences
(c) certificate of registration and airworthiness, crew licences, passenger manifest, load sheet and maintenance manual

15. A continuous red beam directed to an aircraft approaching an aerodrome means:
(a) the aerodrome is unserviceable, and landing should be made elsewhere
(b) the aircraft is forbidden to land for the time being and previous permission is cancelled
(c) give way to other aircraft and continue circling

16. If while flying at night you see a white flashing light ahead which is getting closer, you are:
(a) sighting a captive balloon
(b) approaching an obstruction to navigation
(c) overtaking another aircraft

17. Definition of Solo is:
(a) alone
(b) without instructor
(c) without another pilot's licence holder

18. An aircraft has landed at an aerodrome without runways. The pilot of the following aircraft, with reference to the first shall:
(a) leave it clear on his left and subsequently turn left
(b) leave it clear on his left and subsequently turn right
(c) leave it clear on his right and subsequently turn left

19. For a flight exceeding 500 nm, the following notice is required by the Met Office:
(a) 4 hours
(b) 2 hours
(c) 1 hour

20. A reportable accident occurs to an aircraft in the UK; the following must be sent the details without delay:
(a) the nearest air traffic control unit
(b) the aircraft operator
(c) the Dept. of Transport, Accident Investigation Branch and the local police

21. When two aircraft are approaching head on:
(a) both alter heading to the right
(b) the bigger aircraft alters heading to the right
(c) the smaller aircraft alters heading to the right

22. The aeronautical ground light beacons at civil aerodromes show:
(a) a two-letter morse group in green
(b) a two-letter morse group in red
(c) a rotating red and green

23. Night is defined in the Rules of the Air and Air Traffic Control Regulations as the time between:

(a) half an hour after sunset and half an hour before sunrise
(b) one hour after sunset and one hour before sunrise
(c) half an hour before sunset and half an hour after sunrise

24. A flying machine registered in the UK, having a maximum total authorised weight of more than 5 700 kg, shall when flying at night show lights as follows:
(a) normal green, red and white navigation lights, all steady
(b) normal green, red and white navigation lights, all steady, plus an anti-collision light
(c) normal green, red and white navigation lights, all flashing, alternating with a flashing white light showing in all directions

25. You plan to fly above 3 000 ft amsl outside controlled airspace on a Track of 267°(T), variation 11W. Which of the following Flight Levels is appropriate?
(a) 75
(b) 80
(c) 85

26. An aircraft in difficulties which does not require immediate assistance but is compelled to land may use the following visual signal:
(a) a succession of green pyros
(b) a succession of red pyros
(c) a succession of white pyros

27. When in an aerodrome circuit, base leg call is made:
(a) on completion of the turn on to the base leg
(b) at the end of the downwind leg
(c) when established on the base leg

28. The last aerodrome that, generally, you take-off from for flight abroad is:
(a) health aerodrome
(b) Customs aerodrome
(c) public aerodrome

29. For IFR flight outside controlled airspace at and below 3 000 ft you must:
(a) remain clear of cloud and stay in sight of the surface
(b) fly not less than 1 000 ft above the highest obstacle within 5 nm
(c) select cruising levels according to the quadrantal flight rules

30. All air navigation obstructions listed in the Air Pilot will be lighted if they attain or exceed a height above ground of:
(a) 300 ft
(b) 500 ft
(c) 600 ft

31. In flight over the UK, if a navigation light fails and cannot be immediately repaired, the pilot should:

(a) give a distress signal
(b) land as soon as it is safe to do so
(c) continue to flight plan destination

32. An airmiss report must be followed up by form CA 1094:
(a) within 7 days of the incident
(b) within 7 days of the pilot's recovery from the shock
(c) immediately on landing

33. Red and green stars fired from the ground towards an aircraft signifies:
(a) the aircraft has violated a danger area and must descend immediately
    and land at a suitable aerodrome
(b) the aircraft is approaching a restricted area and should alter heading
(c) it's not long to November 5th

34. A flag showing 12 equal squares coloured alternately red and yellow
displayed near the control tower of an aerodrome signifies:
(a) pilots report here
(b) check direction of take-off with aerodrome control
(c) aircraft may move on the apron and manoeuvring area only as
    instructed by the air traffic control unit at the aerodrome

35. During an initial climb in uncontrolled airspace, a pilot:
(a) must set 1013·2 on the altimeter
(b) must use aerodrome QNH only
(c) may use any setting

36. A SIGMET message contains:
(a) warning of severe weather
(b) routine weather report
(c) important message for VIPs aboard

37 In the UK while navigating by visual reference to a landmark e.g.
a railway line, the rule is to keep such landmark:
(a) to the left of the aircraft
(b) to the right of the aircraft
(c) below the aircraft

38. When flying over an aerodrome where no ATC is operational for
the time being, the pilot should:
(a) keep clear of cloud and not descend below 500 ft above the aerodrome
    elevation
(b) keep 500 ft below cloud
(c) keep 500 ft above cloud

39. In the UK, subject to certain exceptions, an aircraft other than a
helicopter shall not fly over any town at a height of less than 1 500 ft
above the highest obstacle within a radius of:
(a) 1 nm
(b) 3 000 yds
(c) 2 000 ft

40. In flight, you see another flying machine on your right at approximately the same altitude and on a constant bearing; you would normally:
(a) take no action as you have right of way
(b) take suitable avoiding action
(c) flash your navigation lights

Answers

1. (a)	11. (a)	21. (a)	31. (b)
2. (c)	12. (c)	22. (a)	32. (a)
3. (a)	13. (a)	23. (a)	33. (b)
4. (a)	14. (b)	24. (b)	34. (c)
5. (c)	15. (c)	25. (c)	35. (c)
6. (c)	16. (c)	26. (c)	36. (a)
7. (a)	17. (c)	27. (a)	37. (a)
8. (c)	18. (a)	28. (b)	38. (a)
9. (b)	19. (a)	29. (b)	39. (c)
10. (b)	20. (c)	30. (b)	40. (b)

The examination for the PPL in general, going on the form book of previous trials, is set out in three separate papers:

Navigation and Meteorology

Aviation Law

Aircraft Technical

Thirty questions, of the type we have spread around this book, are asked in each paper and the pass mark in each is 70%. This means 21 correct each time, and there are no half marks; your answer is plain right or wrong, and each question carries equal marks. The CAA has a number of authorised examiners to conduct both the written examinations and the flight tests, so you can make arrangements locally through your instructor to take your licence qualifying examinations.

12: Radio aids

Now an informative section to provide some background for the private pilot who wants to get acquainted with some of the radio aids in general use.

A paragraph first on frequency, cycle and wavelength. A radio wave is like an alternating electric current, the electrons of which move about a mean position (Fig. 12.1).

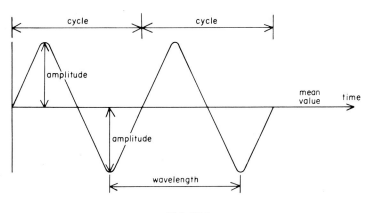

FIG 12.1

A **cycle** is one complete process
Frequency is the number of cycles per second, expressed in Hertz (Hz)
Wavelength is the distance between two successive crests of the wave.

A wave travels at 300 000 000 metres per second: so if two cycles are transmitted in one second, two complete cycles will occupy a space of 300 000 000 metres, which is its wave length.

Thus: Wavelength in metres $= \dfrac{\text{speed of waves in metres per second}}{\text{frequency in cycles per second}}$

Watch the units.
The higher the frequency, the shorter the wavelength, and to avoid getting into large figures:

1 000 cycles/sec = 1 kilohertz (kHz)
1 000 kHz   = 1 megahertz (MHz)
1 000 MHz   = 1 gigahertz (GHz)

and 'cycle per sec' is now obsolete, and the expression Hz, for Hertz, is the replacement: thus kHz, MHz and so on. An example for the mathematically minded:

If transmission frequency is 75 MHz, what is the wavelength?

$$\text{Wavelength in metres} = \frac{\text{Speed in metres}}{\text{Frequency in Hertz}}$$

$$= \frac{300\,000\,000}{75\,000\,000}$$

$$= 4 \text{ metres}$$

For ready reference, there follows a tabulation of the accepted terms for the various ranges of radio frequencies, with some of their characteristics. This is well worth a careful study to help in understanding some of the aids you might use now or eventually – especially when you're thinking of buying something for your aircraft from a gifted salesman.

Designation	Abbreviation	Frequency band	Wavelength
Very Low	VLF	3–30 kHz	100 km–10 km
Low	LF	30–300 kHz	10 km–1 km
Medium	MF	300–3 000 kHz	1 km–100 m
High	HF	3–30 MHz	100 m–10 m
Very High	VHF	30–300 MHz	10 m–1 m
Ultra High	UHF	300–3 000 MHz	1 m–10 cm
Super High	SHF	3 000–30 000 MHz	10 cm–1 cm
Extremely High	EHF	Above 30 000 MHz	Less than 1 cm

Ground wave

Waves which leave the transmitter tangential to the Earth's surface bend with the surface: but they lose energy by contact – and the higher the frequency, the more contact, and therefore the greater loss. The surface is important – the energy loss is greatest over dry soil, least over the sea. The range expectations of a ground wave, as a generalisation are:

LF Loss of energy is low, and ranges of several thousands of miles are obtainable, given sufficient power.

MF 1 000 miles is the maximum range, more usually 300–500 miles, since loss of energy is increased.

HF About 100 miles only, with considerable loss of energy: in fact, increased power does not increase range.

VHF and above. No bending with the surface of the Earth, and only ranges a touch better than line of sight are possible.

Sky wave

Waves leaving the transmitter in a vertical plane may return to Earth, but how and when depends on the height and density of various layers of the ionosphere, the season, the time of day, the angle the signal makes, sun spots and what have you. But sky waves are receivable and usable, and without any more of this heavy theory, we come up with the following table:

Freq.	Ground wave	Sky wave	
		Day	*Night*
LF	Several thousand miles	Too weak to use	Sky waves are present which are a nuisance to ADF operation.
MF	300–500 miles approx.	Too weak to use	Present: ADF suffers.
HF	100 miles	Present, but ranges short. Higher frequency gives longer range as reflection is off higher layer.	Present, and useful. Reflection layer is higher, and ranges therefore increased.
VHF	Quasi-optical	None	None

And in all this, with a sky wave which bounces back to Earth at a distance greater than the range of the ground wave, you could be in an area of 'dead space' where you'll receive damn all from that station.

After this deep exploration into the realm of wave propagation and reception, an outline of some of the radio aids will not go amiss.

Non-Directional Beacons (NDBs) and ADF

These are MF, 300 kHz to 3 000 kHz; however, frequencies in this band are restricted by ICAO to between 200–1 750 kHz, and UK and Europe operate between 255–455 kHz. Signals are emitted in all directions from the transmitter: if the receiver of the airborne equipment called the ADF is tuned to the frequency of a station, the direction of the incoming wave is measured relative to nose of the aircraft – that is, the nose of the aircraft is 000°, or dead ahead.

It is the ground wave which is measured, and the range is about 200 nm by day, 70 nm by night due to interference by sky waves. In fact, at night, the wave is often immeasurable and the erratic movement of the needle serves as a warning (apart from the fact that it's unreadable, and the mean of its oscillation is by no means the best reading); dusk and dawn are quite frightful, and the nearest station is the most hopeful choice at night.

Interference from other MF stations with similar frequencies is improved by the 'Protection Range' afforded by the powers-that-be. This gives a range up to which a particular beacon can be received free from interference from other stations. There are many other adversities to clog up reception at all times, such as static due to cloud or electrical disturbance, mountains and hills between the aircraft and the station, coastal refraction (the bending of a wave passing from a land to a sea surface and vice versa), type of surface, the power of the transmitter, to name but most of them. But at night, sky waves from distant NDBs on similar frequencies can seriously affect the operation of the ADF; their reception cannot be forecast or measured since the height of the ionosphere layer from which the sky waves are reflected is variable. So Protection Range is only guaranteed *during the day.*

The NDB is well on its way out, but there are enough around, at home and abroad, to make an understanding of its uses and limitations worth while.

There was a time when you could use the ordinary broadcasting stations e.g. Droitwich, for ADF purposes. However both in the UK and overseas, authorities are increasing the practice of using the same frequency at a number of locations. Consequently bearings obtained from such stations must be regarded as generally unreliable, so avoid this temptation.

For interest, information or reference, we'll mention a few technicalities leading to a simple table for the operation of the ADF.

Emissions of radio signals are classified according to the characteristics of the signal. These classifications changed in 1982. For NDBs, the classifications are either NON A1A or NON A2A.

NON A1A. Information is conveyed, not by modulation but by causing breaks in the carrier wave (or, in technical language, ON/OFF keying of the carrier) and thus producing morse characters.

NON A2A. Information is conveyed by ON/OFF keying of the modulating signal and not the carrier wave.

Thus, information may be conveyed either by means of breaks in the carrier wave (A1A) or by breaks in the modulated wave (A2A). This makes it imperative to have a control switch which may be used to receive signals with appropriate coding. This switch is usually found on the ADF control box and is named either CW/RT switch or BFO (beat frequency oscillator) or TONE with ON and OFF positions. The first thing necessary to use an NDB is to ascertain its type of emission, otherwise, with CW/RT switch in the wrong place the signal may not be heard, and if heard, may not be identified. This information is found on aerad charts, where the callsign in inverted commas means it is A2A e.g. 'NMN' 331.

If the signal emission type is A2A the question of producing a beat note does not arise, since the signal is audio modulated. A2A signal therefore suggests CW/RT switch in RT position (or BFO or TONE OFF). The following is the summary of use of the switch.

Station Type	When Tuning the Station	When Identifying the Station
NON A1A	CW position (BFO/TONE ON)	CW position (BFO/TONE ON)
NON A2A	CW position (BFO/TONE ON)	RT position (BFO/TONE OFF)

Types of NDBs

1. **Holding and Let-down NDBs:** These are short range NDBs, their main purpose being to serve a location. The type of emission is generally A2A

and the range according to the station requirements, usually of the order of some 10 nm.

2. **En-Route Navigation Aid Beacons.** These are installed along airways to mark reporting points and help en-route navigation. The ranges are controlled by operational requirements, generally between 20 to 50 nm. Usually, the type of emission is A2A.

3. **Long Range Beacons.** These, subject to requirements radiate up to 200 nm during the day; 70 nm at night. Type of emission will generally be A1A.

VHF Omni-directional Radio Range (VOR)

This is widespread, and has now almost entirely replaced the NDB in the UK and USA. It is an en route and homing aid, VHF, and so practically free of static and night effect, more accurate than the ADF, but broadly restricted to line of sight range: this last is much to be borne in mind by private pilots whose flying is so often in the lower altitudes. It provides an infinite number of **magnetic** bearings called 'radials'.

The airborne equipment consists of a special aerial, matched to the frequency band, a receiver which could be used for both VOR and ILS (Instrument Landing System), and an indicator. The indicator consists of three basic components which might all be installed as a single unit or might be installed individually. These components are:

(a) Heading or Bearing Selector
(b) To-From Indicator and
(c) A left/right deviation indicating needle.

Figure 12.2 shows the indicator in two separate units.

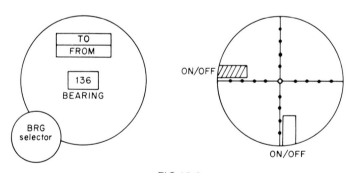

FIG 12.2

Omni-Bearing Selector (OBS) and To/From Indicator

In its simplest terms, a radial is selected for homing, or a radial is read for a bearing. The operation in full and the points to watch therein are not the purpose of this monograph. Suffice it to say that this aid is without vices and the coverage of the country is now extensive. The frequency is 108–118 MHz, at intervals of 0·05 MHz e.g. 112·1, 112·5, 112·2. The range is rather better than optical, about 30 nm at 1 000 ft, 100 nm at 5 000 ft, 120 nm at 10 000 ft, and at no altitude will satisfactory operation be obtained beyond 200 nm. In fact, watch it if you're using it around 100 nm range, but what more can you ask if flying in the UK? With the needle centred on the dial, you're on the radial you've set: or, if you centre the needle at any time, you read off the radial you're therefore on. The finer points come under the practical operation title: an OFF flag appears if there's a transmitter failure, a receiver failure, or the aircraft is out of range; if a transmitter failure occurs, a stand-by automatically takes over (while this is going on, a few minutes usually, the identification signal is **not** transmitted). In addition to the range limitations mentioned, intervening high ground between aircraft and transmitter will block the signal, a point to remember. In the main, accuracy at the receiver is ±2° on 95% of occasions.

Advantages
1. Visual indication, easy to see.
2. Provides infinite number of tracks.
3. Free from static night effect.
4. Ranges can be accurately forecasted before the beacons are sited and thus interference can be avoided.
5. Indicator can be used in conjunction with ILS.
6. It can be frequency paired with DME to give fixes.
7. Incorporates equipment failure warning device.
8. Channel spacing much better than NDBs.

Disadvantages
1. Left/Right indication does not point to the beacon and no continuous bearing information is available unless the RMI is used (but see the next story).
2. Only position lines are obtained unless the aircraft is overhead the beacon or the aid is used in conjunction with DME (see subsequent story).
3. Irregular terrain in vicinity of the transmitter and mountainous countryside can effect accuracy of the bearings.
4. Some early VORs for light aircraft did not operate properly with a number of European Doppler VORs and should have been recalled by manufacturers by now. CAA alerted flying clubs by Pink AIC.

Radio Magnetic Indicator (RMI)
An advance on the NDB, in that the pointer reads off a QDM at once: the scale card is fed with heading information from the aircraft's gyrosyn

compass, or the scale is rotatable, and can be set to the aircraft's Heading Magnetic. Once tuned in, the needle points to the station – and it can be tuned to an NDB or VOR: with two pointers (of different shapes) energised simultaneously, a brace of bearings is obtainable for a fix. So range and accuracy can usually be obtained, since either or both aids – NDB/VOR – can be used together.

Advantages
1. QDM/QDR read directly.
2. Using two beacons, instantaneous fixes may be obtained.
3. Very useful guide when initially joining a radial for homing on VOR.
4. Can be used for homing.

Distance Measuring Equipment (DME)
Off into radar, with interrogators and transponders, in the UHF frequency band, at around 1 000 MHz, this aid gives a range to the aircraft from a DME station as a straightforward display in figures. It's a slant range actually, but this is not of importance at over 10 nm: at 10 nms, it is in error by less than a mile: overhead, it will read your height in nms. The range isn't terrific, about 110 nm at 10 000 ft, but coupled with a co-sited VOR is clearly very valuable indeed, for you have a range and a bearing. The coverage is extensive. Airways flying is now largely defined by VOR/DME stations, and since you will be using the aid from an altitude below the specified height of the airway, you must be aware of the limitations.

One snag is that the VOR/DME must be co-sited: tune in the VOR, and you automatically tune the associated DME i.e. they are **frequency paired**: one callsign only is heard. But if you hear the VOR callsign (once every 10 seconds) and the DME callsign (once every 30 seconds) with Z as the last letter of one of them, the stations can be treated as co-incident, though they do not obey the rigid rules laid down for co-siting (at or below 2 000 ft apart for en route aids, 100 ft for approach).

If entirely different identifiers are heard, check the positions of the stations – they are not coincident by any means.

Incidentally, DME used to be called TACAN, and VOR/DME called VOR-TAC: still are by the venerable.

Uses
1. Provides fixes when used with VOR.
2. Range indications are very useful when carrying out instrument approaches.
3. Eases the task of the ATC in identifying when an aircraft reports its position in terms of range and bearing from a VOR/DME station.

4. When two aircraft using DME are flying on the same track, the positive ranges from these aircraft enable ATC to maintain accurate separation.

The cost of installing VOR/DME is decreasing with demand; display is getting neater, with bearings and distances shown as plain figures. Do remember the drawbacks, though, particularly the range limitations at low altitudes.

Instrument Landing System (ILS)

This is worth a mention, though it's an Instrument Rating aid, since it uses the same dial as the VOR, and panels are available with it incorporated.

The pilot has his position indicated relative to the centre line of the runway, and relative to the glide path or descent angle: he can thus arrive over the threshold at the optimum touch-down point without any assistance from ground controllers and, within reason, independent of the weather: pointer movements are large for small deviations from the glide path, and the information is presented on a continuous basis for the particular runway.

Consider the vertical needle first (Fig, 12.3): on approach you follow the needle: if it's to the left, fly left. You're on the centre line when the needle is centred. This signal is sent out by the 'localiser' transmitter.

FIG 12.3

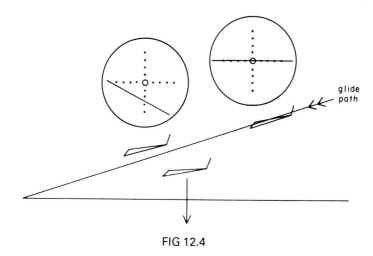

FIG 12.4

Now the horizontal needle (Fig. 12.4): if the needle is above the centre line, fly up: if centralised, you're on the glide path. The position of the needle is heavily weighted towards safety – full scale 4 or 5 dots (depending on the instrument) is 0·7°. And the CAA strongly recommends that *half full scale deflection fly up* be the maximum permitted i.e. on a 4-dots scale, if you have a 2-dot fly up reading, you *must* fly up immediately.

This display (Fig. 12.5) indicates, on approach, fly up and turn left. Frequencies are VHF, much in the same area as VOR, and only the localiser frequency is given: the glide path will be automatically tuned, as it is frequency paired to the localiser.

Range is up to 25 nm.

Perhaps that's enough for an acquaintanceship: there are details of monitoring, position, warning signals, rather outside our present province.

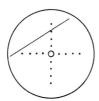

FIG 12.5

13: Aircraft loading/Fire hazard

The basic essentials for a safe flight from a loading point of view may be given in the following two don'ts and a do:

(i) never exceed your aircraft's take-off weight
(ii) never exceed your aircraft's landing weight
(iii) keep the aircraft's centre of gravity (C of G) within its prescribed limits.

The C of G limits are laid down by the manufacturer, and for the Commercial Pilot's licence you will need to learn how to calculate the position of the C of G for various loading arrangements.

Overloading causes unsatisfactory control responses, to say nothing of the possibility of structural damage to the aircraft. If the loading is unevenly distributed and the C of G is moved outside its limits the control responses become abnormal, trimming is difficult or even impossible, and the aircraft may become unstable or unmanageable. It doesn't take much imagination to foresee the difficulty of attempting take-off or landing with the aircraft's control responses seriously impaired.

In calculating the load you are about to carry, you must include the weight of the crew and passengers (see our book 'Aviation Law for Pilots'), the baggage and/or cargo weight, and the weight of fuel and oil. When you have totalled these items compare the figure with the maximum all-up weight for your type of aircraft to ensure that you are within the permitted limit. The term maximum all-up weight may be defined as the maximum weight at which the aircraft is permitted to fly within normal design restrictions. All-up weight, in its turn, is defined as the total weight of the aircraft in its operational condition.

Other definitions that you should know in connection with aircraft loading are the following.

Tare weight: the empty weight or, more precisely, the weight of an aircraft equipped to a minimum scale, plus the weight of coolants, residual fuel and oil, and residual de-icing and hydraulic fluids.

Basic weight: this is tare weight plus any load necessarily carried in order to meet a given requirement.

Pay load: this is the weight of passengers plus cargo that the aircraft is carrying or is designed to carry.

IN THE EVENT OF FIRE

The likelihood of a fire taking place is remote in modern aircraft. However, when such incidents do occur they most commonly originate with the engine although others have occurred in burnt-out electric motors for operating undercarriage or flaps. In the event of an engine fire your immediate action is to turn off the fuel. Then, open the throttle fully in order to clear the carburettor and fuel lines. Switch off the engine and operate the fire extinguisher. If the propeller can be feathered, feather it in order to prevent it from windmilling, and to reduce drag.

The following are typical questions the PPL student should be prepared to answer, based on this and Chapters 2 and 3. They may be asked in this form in relation to your flight test, but will be in multi-choice form in the written examination.

1. What are the forces acting on an aircraft in level flight?
2. Describe the forces acting on an aircraft in a climb, glide, turn.
3. Why does the stalling speed increase in a turn?
4. What movement of ailerons takes place in left bank?
5. What is the primary effect of rudder?
6. If one wing should drop before the other in a stall, what would be the corrective action and why?
7. What do you understand by the following:
   (a) angle of attack
   (b) stalling angle
   (c) relative airflow
   (d) chord line.
8. What do you understand by induced drag?
9. What forces act on an aircraft in a glide?
10. What is the purpose of the flaps?
11. What is the purpose of slats?
12. Define the following:
    (a) longitudinal stability
    (b) lateral stability
    (c) directional stability
13. What is the firing order of a four cylinder, in line engine?
14. Describe the four strokes of the four-stroke engine.
15. Why does the inlet valve open just before the end of the exhaust stroke?
16. What service should an advance carburettor provide?
17. What is the purpose of an acceleration pump in a carburettor?
18. What is the purpose of mixture control?
19. Why are fuels coloured?
20. Explain what you understand by detonation.
21. What two purposes are served by the engine lubrication system?
22. What is an aircraft's normal axis?
23. What is an aircraft's basic weight?
24. Which of lift or drag is more affected when only a small amount of flap is lowered?
25. What is the purpose of dihedral on mainplanes?

14: Now hear this

Or what the CAA has seen fit to issue circulars or warnings about recently; or what we have heard you should be reminded about; or we've been told has not been adequately stressed, yea, even omitted from our writings. They are split into four main headings, not always clear-cut – Reporting, Medical, Radio, Safety and Sundry Procedures.

REPORTING
Airmiss
The procedure is detailed in the Law Chapter, but has evidently not been followed in a number of cases: this has caused delay, and the other aircraft has not been traceable. The CAA want to stress that the investigation is carried out by a group made up of civil and military pilots, and operators of diverse aviation backgrounds, with no legal significance. The investigation seeks to determine the cause of the airmiss and to take such action as will reduce the possibility of a recurrence. The anonymity of individuals and companies concerned is preserved. So check the procedure – first report by radio, written report within 7 days, and await the findings and remedial action recommended. Abroad, you must follow the State's reporting procedure where the airmiss occurred.

This circular was sent out on pink, so it has some muscle.

Occurrences
First of all, look up 'Notification of Accidents' in the Law chapter: it has not altered one jot or tittle. But a 'Reportable Occurrence' is a touch confusing – it is any incident relating to an aircraft, or any defect or malfunctioning of the aircraft or its equipment which, if not corrected, would endanger the aircraft or any person; or any defect in, or malfunctioning of, any facility on the ground used or intended to be used in connection with the operation of the aircraft which would have a similar result. Now if you can't readily differentiate between an Accident and a Reportable Occurrence, report it as an Accident; believe it or not, it will be dealt with in the Chief Inspector of Accidents department, or sent to the Safety Data Unit. In fact, the liaison between the two departments is fluid. Their main worry is that any delay in reporting 'affects seriously the efficacy of the investigation'.

Also a Confidential Human Factors Incident Reporting Programme (CHIRP) has been introduced in the United Kingdom by the CAA run by the RAF Institute of Medicine, which all aircrew are encouraged to use. Human failure is known to be the cause of about 80% of accidents and 60% of fatals. A human factors incident is one in which either a crew member's action or failure to act caused (or could have) a potentially hazardous situation or the aircraft's equipment or operating procedure could have contributed to the crew member's error. This programme supplements the Mandatory Occurrence Reporting Scheme. If report forms are not available from briefing or crew rooms, further information and forms can be obtained from:

> Confidential Reports
> FREEPOST
> RAF Institute of Aviation Medicine
> Farnborough, Hants.
> Tel: Aldershot (0252) 24461 Ext 4375

Communications on Safety Matters

Any communications about significant safety matters should be sent to the address below, and if no receipt of the letter is received within 7–10 days, contact the appropriate Division again:

For matters relating to airworthiness:

> Director General Airworthiness
> Civil Aviation Authority
> Brabazon House
> Redhill, Surrey RH1 1SQ. Tel: Redhill 65966 Ext. 205.

For matters relating to operations:

> Director General Operations
> Civil Aviation Authority
> Aviation House
> 129 Kingsway
> London WC2B 6NN. Tel: 01-450 6922 Ext, 438.

For matters relating to the National Air Traffic Services:

> Deputy Controller
> National Air Traffic Services
> Civil Aviation Authority
> CAA House
> 45–59 Kingsway
> London WC2B 6TE. Tel: 01-379 7311 Ext. 2782.

MEDICAL
Personal Injuries and Illness

(a) The attention of ALL licence holders (the capitals are the CAAs), other than R/T, is drawn to the ANO which states:

1. any personal injury which incapacitates the holder from undertaking the function of his licence or
2. any illness ditto ditto for a period of 20 days or more shall inform

the CAA as soon as possible of the injury, and after the twentieth day in the case of illness.

(b) There are usually several pink AICs valid drawing pilots' attention to health/medical matters. For example, the need for immediate first aid in the event of skin contact with kerosene or other aviation fuels.

(c) **Pilots and spectacles.** Because pilots are allowed to wear spectacles to correct their vision, CAA offers specialist advice from its Medical Dept HQ and offers general warnings. If spectacles are only needed for reading, CAA advise that pilots should never use full-lens glasses whilst flying, but use half-moon or lower segment lenses instead. Also pilots are warned against spectacles with thick frames or with photo-sensitive lenses because of their restriction of vision.

(d) **Radiation hazard.** Pilots are alerted to the need to keep at least 0·5 nm laterally and 1 000 ft vertically from Airborne Early Warning (or AWAC) aircraft to avoid radiation hazards emanating from the large bulbous nose of the Nimrod or the rotodome mounted on USAF aircraft.

(e) **Hypoxia.** The ANO lays down the rules for use of oxygen in aircraft. The CAA has seen a need to draw attention to the fact that although many aircraft have unpressurised crew and passenger compartments they are capable of flight at altitudes where the air is too thin for efficient breathing and hypoxia will occur. The pink AIC details the physiological effects, breathing air at altitude, effect of decompression and general guidance on the use of oxygen. If you are going to operate at relatively low level, this will not be your problem. If however you move up-market to flying at higher levels, you must read this thoroughly.

(f) **Medication and alcohol.** Minor ailments which would not prevent a person doing a satisfactory job in a variety of businesses on the ground, could well be responsible for aviation accidents CAA say. Particularly identified as incompatible with flying are antibiotics, tranquillisers, anti-depressants, sedatives, stimulants, antihistamines, analgesics, blood-pressure pills, together with the need for a recovery period for such activities as blood donation, anaesthetics (including local and general dental treatment). The pink AIC also takes the opportunity to warn off pilots from drugs and, as regards alcohol, states 'Pilots should not fly for at least 8 hours after taking small amounts of alcohol and proportionately longer if larger amounts are consumed'. A similar AIC is directed to ATCOs.

RADIO
Radio Procedures

These have been modified here and there, with respect to Acknowledgement of ATC messages, which for safety, you should *always* read back, though they do give a list of occasions when you must; and with respect to Information to be passed to ATC, which is all rather a mouthful. It can be boiled down to the fact that if you have a request to make, ATC want to know who you are, where you're from and where you're going to, and anything else important to your request. Oh yes, your aircraft type, give it after your callsign. The whole bag of tricks is called a 'standardised format'. To conform to international practice, UK changed from 'overshoot' to 'go around' and despite pleas to revert back to the original, longstanding term, has kept to this decision.

The CAA use a pink circular to inform civil pilots of a military flight procedure available for use where radio failure is worsened by uncertainty of position. It emphasises the procedure is a last-resort measure not replacing recognised procedures such as transponder codes 7600/7700. Basically the procedure is, while maintaining safe terrain clearance, to fly an equilateral triangle at least twice. The 120° turns should be made as tight as practicable and the triangle sides each 2 minutes long at speeds up to 300 kt TAS and 1 minute long at higher speeds.

Flight without radio: Code of Practice

This means aircraft without radio, or radio-equipped aircraft flying at aerodromes without radio.

The Code of Practice is as follows 'to enhance flight safety considerably'.

Before Take-off

1. Tell ATC, AFIS or a responsible person, of your intentions, and note any instructions or information given to you.

2. On a local flight, check that the visibility is at least 3 km (more if your circuit speed is above 100 kt), that there is a cloud ceiling of at least 600 ft over the highest obstacle within 4 nm of the aerodrome and 800 ft at the aerodrome itself. If you know your aerodrome well the first two figures could be reduced to 2 km and 300 ft, but the ceiling at the aerodrome should still be 800 ft.

3. On a cross country:
   (a) Check you have up to date maps covering the intended route and alternative aerodrome.
   (b) Check that the weather en route and at destination will give 5 km visibility and a 1 500 ft cloud ceiling or better.
   (c) Check you have full information on the destination and alternative aerodromes, especially the aerodrome height and local procedures.
   (d) Check NOTAMS.
   (e) Obtain prior permission if required.
   (f) Prepare a navigation flight plan and aim to arrive before sunset.
   (g) File an ATS Flight Plan, or book-out. A Flight Plan is particularly important if the flight is over water or sparsely populated territory, to ensure that the search and rescue organisation will be alerted promptly if the need arises.

4. Position yourself to the right of anyone taking off ahead of you.

En Route

1. Remain VMC.

2. Stay below cloud unless map reading from above cloud is practicable (i.e. if there are 3 oktas or less of cloud and the visibility below is more than 5 km.)

3. Turn back or divert in good time if deteriorating weather starts to impair navigation.

On Arrival – (Unless otherwise instructed before take-off)

1. Fly over the aerodrome above circuit height (2 000 ft above aerodrome height if possible) to inspect the signals square and the wind sock, and to establish the position of any other aircraft operating at the aerodrome.

2. Make a normal circuit keeping a good look out on both sides of the aircraft. Bank the wings while looking. Do not attempt a straight in approach or a shortened circuit. Keep a sharp look out for any light signals or pyrotechnic signals from the aerodrome. (To assist other radio equipped aircraft, if you have a radio, listen out and make the standard calls before joining and at the appropriate points in the circuit.)

3. Join the circuit on the dead side.

4. Ensure that you are down to circuit height before turning cross wind.

5. Make the first cross wind leg close to the upwind end of the active runway (or the aerodrome boundary).

6. Position yourself well behind other aircraft in the circuit, or, if you are considerably faster than they are, well outside them.

7. Aim to land to the right of anyone landing ahead of you or taking-off.

8. If there is no paved runway, stop, turn left and check it is clear to taxi in.

9. Park so as not to cause an obstruction.

10. Close your flight plan or book in.

AND REMEMBER – ALL THE TIME YOU ARE IN THE COCKPIT KEEP A GOOD LOOKOUT.

Limitations of NDB and ADF

CAA are worried that with the fairly world-wide replacement of MF NDBs by VOR, pilots might lose sight of their limitations. NDBs are still in use as navigation and approach aids, and as a lead-in to instrument approach systems, so, until they disappear entirely, we summarise the conditions which contribute to potentially dangerous errors.

Static Interference
Station Interference
Night Effect
Mountain Effect
Coastal Refraction
Absence of failure warning system.

It has to be stressed that at comparatively short distances, i.e. less than 50 nautical miles over which NDBs are most commonly used, the most potentially dangerous errors are those resulting from all types of precipitation static, thunderstorms and station interference (particularly at night). When these are experienced, the ADF system should be used only when necessary and then with extreme caution; VHF aids are much less affected and these should be used in preference wherever possible. Cross-checking on the accuracy of ADF indications, by reference to other available navigational aids, is not only a matter of good airmanship but also a most necessary safeguard wherever any difficulty is experienced in the reception or identification of the intended NDB.

Much of this has been mentioned in the Radio Aids chapter, but we don't apologise for repeating it here.

SAFETY

It's all safety, really, but a few of the CAA's pink 'uns are mentioned here which are of potent significance.

Insect blockage of Pitot tubes and Fuel Tank Vents

Sounds like a plague of locusts in Egypt, or marabunta in South America, but seven cases were reported at one aerodrome, and two others elsewhere: four aircraft aborted take-off, or returned at once due to no ASI reading, and one of them had only been parked for $1\frac{1}{2}$ hours: even hangared aircraft were found to have their pitot blocked when inspected after these discoveries.

In another case, the fuel vent was blocked by foliage and an insect grub, and the aircraft was damaged on forced landing due to fuel starvation from a half-full tank. Is there no limit to the hazards that beset us; O Lord?

Make sure, therefore, that static and fuel vents, and pitot tubes are clear before flight; blockings should be cleared by properly qualified personnel; and even if parking for only a short time, fit the correct covers; remove them before flight, remember. If you've not got the correct covers, make the covers you've got as conspicuous as possible, and avoid the use of invisible adhesive tape.

Bird strikes

All bird strikes are reportable using Form CA 1282 which has gradually been modified over the years. Make sure you use the correct version. It has the address of CAA's Safety Data & Analysis Unit already printed on it. The remains of the bird, properly wrapped, go to MAFF *not* CAA.

Life Jacket/Life Raft Serviceability

This is a very old chestnut, but of the greatest importance for a flight over water. Since flotation equipment is usually installed prior to a particular flight, it is recommended that you insist the pack is labelled with the date when the next servicing is due. If you've got your own, follow closely the recommended procedures for maintenance, so you're always ready for that impulsive trip to Le Touquet.

Visual illusions in flight

This outlines some of the hazards which these illusions may introduce, particularly on approach to land.

They fall under one or more of the following headings:

Sloping approach terrain
Sloping runways
Runway width
Rain on the windscreen
Featureless approach terrain
Runway lighting intensity
Shallow fog
Rain showers.

Sloping approach terrain. On approach, with the ground sloping upward, the pilot can get the illusion that the aircraft is too high: with down-slope terrain that he is too low.

Sloping runways. The illusion is similar to that of sloping approach terrain.

Runway width. Decreasing the distance from the runway can give the illusion of shortening the parallel lines of the runway seen in perspective. The wider the runway, the shorter it appears: also, a wide runway tends to give the pilot a feeling he is lower than he really is.

Rain. Heavy rain can diffuse the glow of approach or runway lights, causing them to appear less intense, and the pilot feels he is farther away than he really is. But **light rain** on the windscreen can double the size of the runway lights, and he thinks he's nearer. It's never-ending. Refraction of light caused by a wet windscreen can give the illusion that the pilot is not properly lined up with the runway, and this illusion can be considerable – CAA quote 200 feet at 1 nm from the threshold.

Featureless approach terrain. This is well-known eyesight problem, where no references are available to judge height, the pilot thinks he's higher than he is, and a premature descent is made. Snow over the complete field makes height over the runway difficult, and the problem is accentuated in poor visibility of course. A very experienced pilot landed short of the runway on a Canadian airfield under these conditions, though he may have been too proud to wear glasses.

Runway lighting intensity. Bright lights appear closer to the observer – and runway lights in a darkened area will appear closer than they really are.

Shallow fog. We've had this one in the Meteorology chapter (Fig. 9.16) since the first edition. Take another look at it. On entering the fog layer, only a runway light or two may be visible, giving the illusion of nose-up. Corrective action for this apparent condition is rather dangerous.

Rain showers. An isolated rain shower on approach can give the illusion that the horizon is lower than it really is, and a corrective though erroneous lowering of the nose, or decrease of power, could be made.

Horizons in layer cloud. When flying between cloud layers, avoid using the clouds as a substitute horizon. Cloud layers are seldom parallel to the Earth's surface.

General. This is a digest of a thoroughly researched report and of a learned text on Aviation Physiology, with a view to disturbing your confidence: your awareness of some of the hazards should in fact increase it. Finally, bear in mind that fatigue will make the illusions worse.

Altimeters

Before flight, ensure that:

1. rotation of the barometric adjustment control knob results in a movement of the pressure setting scale and the altimeter pointer.

2. forward pressure on the knob during rotation doesn't disengage the barometric scale from the altimeter pointer.

3. QNH when set agrees with aerodrome elevation, or QFE reads zero. Evidently, a pilot in flight set QNH, and the altimeter setting scale became detached from the altimeter pointer. This resulted in a large altimeter error, and you can say that again. Thought we'd mention it.

Altimeter setting in deep lows. Although British altimeter subscales range from 800 to 1 050 millibars, some American altimeters have 950 mb as the lowest subscale setting. The AIC first urges replacement of the US altimeter with a British-made model. If this is not done, advice is offered on action to be taken when there is abnormally low pressure. The first recommendation is not to take off if QNH is below 950 mb at departure or destination and IMC. Secondly, if it is VMC and very low pressure (i.e. below 950 mb), on any flight made the subscale should be set to the lowest possible value and greatest care taken to ensure terrain clearance and to maintain the ATC-cleared altitude.

The Aeronautical Emergency Service and Procedures for Pilots in distress, urgency or difficulty

This pink'un has some very good advice for the private pilot. The bare bones of action to be taken are given in the Law Chapter, but this circular is full of practical information.

121·5 MHz is the emergency frequency for aircraft in distress or in urgent need of assistance, **when assistance cannot be obtained through normal channels.** The Emergency Service and the procedures to be followed are also, however, intended for a pilot in difficulties which do not warrant declaring a 'distress' or 'urgency' state.

In the first case, if the safe conduct of a flight is in doubt, get in touch with the ATS, or FIS, on the radio. They will initiate assistance, and will call in the Emergency Service required. The important thing is the **early** call on normal channels when you are concerned that danger or serious difficulty may arise unless some advice or assistance is given now. Don't be misunderstood – a vague request for a confirmation of position will not be given the same priority as 'I'm lost'.

An emergency communications **and aid** service on 121·5 MHz is continuously available, and it has a wide network for fixing and initiating assistance. But VDF fixing is time-consuming, and not frightfully successful below 3 000 feet.

In distress and urgency, a pilot will broadcast a MAYDAY or PAN on 121·5 MHz, addressed to no one in particular, and will stay on that frequency until told by the Emergency Controller who has answered the call. The message thereupon will give call sign, type of aircraft, nature of emergency, qualification of the pilot, intention, position, FL/altitude, Heading. The qualification of the pilot is not a statutory requirement, but is recommended, since the controller will endeavour to match his instructions to the ability of the pilot: and if the pilot cannot comply with instructions, he should say so (e.g. he is incapable of flying in cloud).

In 'difficulty', the Emergency Service is just as readily available, but call up the appropriate ATCC on 121·5 MHz. So if you're unsure of your position i.e. you're lost, use this service. Inexperienced civil pilots are invited to use the callsign prefix TYRO when communicating in these circumstances.

Practice emergencies

These are highly recommended: the call is made to the appropriate ATCC on 121·5 MHz: listen out first though to make sure that the frequency is not being used for real. Prefix the call with 'Practice'; an example is to use the intended destination as a 'request for diversion', not upsetting the flight at all. Beware of trying to avoid landing fees by calling a practice emergency, though: landing fees are only waived in a real emergency. Some spiv obviously tried it.

Propeller feathering

Most propellers fitted to light twin piston-engined aeroplanes are designed so that they do not feather at low rpm so that after shut-down at the end of a flight the re-start is not made with a feathered propeller. However a pink AIC reminds pilots of such aircraft of the need for practice to ensure a slick performance when in flight a propeller has to be feathered for real, before the u/s engine's revs drop below 1 000 whilst maintaining the speed for best engine-out rate of climb.

A separate pink AIC reminds Flying Instructors and Training Captains of the precautions to be taken when simulating engine failure in flight of multi-engine aeroplanes, both pre-flight and in-flight, as well as in handling and performance. Another good read for all pilots.

Avoidance of Controlled Airspace

Unauthorised penetration of controlled airspace or aerodrome traffic zones has caused many incidents and airmisses. Pilots experiencing navigational difficulties in the vicinity of such airspace sometimes seem reluctant to tell ATS of their troubles – especially when the conduct of the flight depends on visual ground reference.

Controlled airspace and aerodrome traffic zone infringements can occur through the misuse of navigational aids and inadequate flight preparation. Pilots should ensure that they can correctly use and interpret navigational equipment carried in the aircraft and should take training specifically to this end, especially before attempting flight near controlled airspace.

Frost, snow and ice

These are **all** hazards, and pre-flight preparation is vital: in flight, Flight Manual instructions concerning the use of anti- and de-icing equipment should be strictly adhered to.

Pre-flight. Free the aircraft of all these deposits; when using approved de-icing fluid, pay particular attention to flaps, control surfaces, and their hinge mechanisms. Clear the lot – any uncleared frost, ice, or snow can cause an imbalance, and any left in the hinge mechanisms can re-freeze in flight.

In-flight. If you've no de-icer on your aircraft, stay at home if icing is forecast. In flight, switch on the de-icing equipment as soon as there's even a suspicion of icing conditions, **before** it starts to form. See the Icing section in the Meteorology chapter. The expanding boot type de-icers on the leading edge are, of course, only effective after the ice has formed.

Should ice be suspected on the leading edge of the tailplane, don't lower the flaps: this could cause tailplane stalling, with a consequent loss of control. Select flaps up at once if, in suspect conditions, control difficulties are encountered as they are lowered.

Carburettor icing. This is covered in the Meteorology and Power Plant chapters. The gist of the CAA's pink circular is all there, but the Authority sadly points out that despite previous AICs, over the years there, has been an average of 10 occurrences per annum in the UK (of which 6 were accidents) reported which the Safety Data and Analysis Unit considered were or may have been caused by carburettor icing.

Danger Areas – Advice to Pilots

There is danger in – **or near** – designated Danger Areas. There is no compulsion for a civil aircraft to avoid the majority of Danger Areas, but they are by definition places where activities dangerous to the flight of aircraft exist at specified times. There is no future in flying through one such which looks inactive but may just drop a load of parachutists from 10 000 feet, or a high speed military aircraft swoops up your jacksie at a great rate of knots (and he's thinking about his target anyway). So keep out, and keep well away.

General Aviation Flights over France

Make sure you've the correct maps, and have done adequate flight planning. Complaints of infringement of French prohibited, restricted and danger areas by private pilots will not only cause the pilots concerned a lot of trouble, but may lead to a limitation of private VFR flights there.

Air displays

The summer season sees a sequence of NOTAMs giving warnings of displays. Non-participating aircraft should keep away and not be tempted to stooge around the edge of the area to get a good view. Jet formation aerobatic teams are obviously most vulnerable in such areas.

Incorrect fuel

Because of difficulties at times of obtaining relatively small quantities of Aviation Gasoline (AVGAS), CAA responded to a request by granting permission for the use of Motor Gasoline (MOGAS) in certain general aviation aeroplanes, (listed in an Airworthiness Notice) after engine and flight testing. Pilots should use MOGAS in these aircraft only and *it must be obtained from a UK aerodrome installation.*

Another serious problem occurs if a piston-engine aircraft is refuelled with jet fuel (JET) by mistake, because when pure JET reaches the engine it stops it. A mix of AVGAS and JET will probably cause detonation and major engine damage. The CAA consider the risk is enhanced on aeroplanes boldly emblazoned TURBO, which are fitted with piston engines which are turbo-charged. The recommended safety precautions are for piston engine aircraft operators to:

1. Remove any TURBO markings.

2. Mark all over-wing filler points (and any filler-cap covers) with a coloured surround and an annotation:

Red – AVGAS

outlining the colour patch with a white margin. Operators should similarly mark ground refuelling installations.

3. Fit standardised restricted filler points to the aircraft tanks and refuelling nozzles to the fuel supply point. Then a 2·6 inch (67 mm) JET nozzle won't go into a 2·3 inch (49 mm) AVGAS tank aperture but a 40 mm AVGAS spout will.

Flying over and near high ground

Although we mentioned this in the Meteorology chapter under 'Standing Waves', just a reminder that the hazards from severe turbulence, downdraughts, icing etc., are such that the CAA has a permanently current AIC of a dozen pages or so drawing pilots' attention and offering advice.

Wake turbulence

A long well-illustrated AIC which all light aircraft pilots should heed when their flights take them to share an aerodrome with the big boys. Depending on runway, wind-direction and speed, atmospheric stability, so differing problems will occur when taking off or landing a light aircraft up to 2 to 3 minutes behind a big jet (or even some small ones).

Using disused aerodromes

In contrast to the preceding paragraph, you may contemplate the quiet attraction of landing at a disused or partly used aerodrome. Be warned that the surface may have become unsafe for use anyway, together with the risk of the presence of people, animals, fences, overhead wires, equipment such as tractors, turf-cutters etc., not to mention hardstanding areas used for storage, banger-racing or what-have-you. If you have to use such a field in an emergency, if possible do a low-level pass and precautionary approach.

Carriage of passengers' portable electronic equipment

Although probably not a risk in a commercial airliner, a passenger in a small aeroplane using electronic games, computers etc., may cause radio interference. The most likely to be affected is the ADF receiver from equipment with light-emitting displays (LED). Monitor any such use to see if there is interference and if there is, see that the electronic equipment is switched off.

Piloting old aircraft and replicas

It is not always appreciated just how much designers have improved the flying characteristics of light aeroplanes. Many older types (of aeroplanes, that is) have their own characteristics or 'quirks' and certainly less margin for error. The AIC identifies less stability, different control forces needed, limited stall warning, wing-dropping, out-of-wind landing habits etc. and sensibly concludes. 'Finally do not be too proud to arrange, whenever possible, a proper flight demonstration and check by someone who is competent on a strange type. Such aeroplanes can be unforgiving towards pilots who are insensitive to their peculiarities.'

Crossing International Frontiers
A Flight Plan **must** be filed.

The point and estimated time of crossing must be entered on the Flight Plan.

The first point of arrival, and last point of departure must be at a Customs Airport.

Air Traffic Services outside regulated airspace
A series of Information Circulars describe the Air Traffic Services (ATS) that are available to civil aircraft in flight within the UK airspace outside Controlled, Special Rules and Advisory Airspace:

Service at Aerodromes
Apart from the data we have already given on page 141, we should remind you that the type of service provided at an aerodrome, together with the period that the aerodrome is available, is notified in the AGA section of the Air Pilot (Schedule of Hours):

Service	*Callsign suffix*
Air Traffic Control	TOWER/GROUND/APPROACH
Service	ZONE RADAR/DIRECTOR
Aerodrome Flight Information	INFORMATION
Service	
Air/Ground Communication	RADIO
Station	

Some aerodromes list 2 services, sometimes 3. They are not provided simultaneously as a mix of services only one service is provided at any one time.

Radar and Non-Radar Services
Outside regulated airspace there are two services available: Advisory (RAS) and Information (RIS). Both are subject to equipment, its coverage and the controller's workload.

The controller will warn the pilot if he expects limitations on the radar service that he can offer such as:

(a) when the aircraft is near the lateral or vertical limits of solid radar cover,

(b) when the aircraft is near or in areas of high traffic density,

(c) when the aircraft is near areas of permanent echoes or weather 'returns',

(d) when the controller considers the performance of his radar is suspect,

(e) when the controller is only using SSR.

A pilot must request radar service – either RAS or RIS – and should not assume he has the service until the controller tells him so, probably after an identification procedure (turns or SSR code). The pilot remains responsible for terrain clearance.

Radar Advisory Service (RAS)

The conditions are:

(a) May be requested under any flight rules or met. conditions.

(b) Controllers will expect the aircraft to accept radar vectors or level allocations which may require flight in IMC. Pilots who are unable to fly in IMC should only accept a RAS whilst weather conditions permit compliance with ATC advice.

(c) When a pilot chooses not to comply with advisory avoiding action, he must inform the controller and he is then responsible for initiating any avoiding action that may subsequently prove necessary.

(d) The pilot must advise the controller before changing heading or flight level.

(e) Information on non-participating, conflicting traffic will be passed until the confliction is resolved.

(f) There is no legal requirement for flights outside regulated airspace to comply with instructions because of the advisory nature of the service. However, pilots will be assumed to be complying with ATC instructions unless they state otherwise.

Radar Information Service (RIS)

The controller informs the pilot of the bearing, distance and, if known, the level of conflicting traffic BUT no avoiding action is offered. The pilot is responsible for maintaining separation whether or not he has been passed traffic information. RIS conditions are:

(a) May be requested under any flight rules or met. conditions.

(b) Manoeuvring flights when frequent changes of heading or flight level involved – RIS passes information on conflicting traffic. Pilot chooses manoeuvring area and flight level, but controller can suggest an area too.

(c) Only updating on conflicting traffic given by controller when either the pilot requests or a definite hazard arises.

(d) Pilot advises controller if changing level, level band or route.

(e) RIS may be offered by controller when RAS impracticable.

(f) Can be upgraded to RAS subject to the controller's workload.

Non-Radar Services
Procedural service
Standard separation minima are provided between participating aircraft for example in holding patterns, flying ADRs, approach control or when radar not available.

Flight Information Service (FIS)
Designed to provide information to help the safe and efficient conduct of flight, it includes:
(a) weather,
(b) changes of serviceability of navigation and approach aids,
(c) conditions at aerodromes.
The procedure has been covered in Chapter 11, Aviation Law.

Aerodrome Traffic Rules
1. An aircraft commander must give notice of arrival or departure to the person in charge of the aerodrome, or the ATCU or aerodrome flight information unit.
2. The aerodrome operator's permission must be sought for the movement on the ground of aircraft, persons or vehicles.
3. Permission to fly in an Aerodrome Control Zone is only required for:
Government i.e. military, research, Aerodromes.
CAA owned or managed aerodrome.
Aerodromes with ATC or AFIS units.
At other aerodromes, permission is not required and this includes take-off and landing, but watch the rules for movement on the aerodrome.
A check of the status is thus needed with regard to these rules – except, of course, in the case of 'force majeure'.

Take-off, Climb and Landing Performance of Light, General Aviation Aeroplanes
The aircraft must be pre-flight checked that is has adequate performance for the proposed flight: can it get airborne in the take-off distance available? Can it climb in the ambient temperature from the aerodrome i.e. is it over-weight? and so on. It is essential to be aware of the performance capabilities and limitations of the aircraft. Its performance can only be based on the **manual designated by the CAA** on its Certificate of Airworthiness.

Factors affecting field and climb performance. And by 'field' is meant take-off and landing. The main factors are weather, terrain and aircraft state and before flight, the pilot must consider:
(a) aircraft all up weight

(b) airfield altitude and temperature at departure and destination
(c) take-off distance available, state of the runway
(d) W/V at departure and forecast W/V at destination
(e) obstacles in the flight path after take-off
(f) obstacles en route
(g) landing distance available and whether the runway is downhill, wet, icy or snow covered.
(h) the consequences of engine failure and the ability to make a safe forced landing.

In all these factors, even a slight discrepancy, if that's the word, can be remarkable in its effect. This pink AIC gives the % corrections pilots should apply for both take-off and landing.

Flight planning
(a) Watch the take-off run required doesn't exceed the take-off run available.
(b) Similarly the take-off distance.
(c) Are obstacles in the take-off flight path to be cleared safely?
(d) Is the aircraft correctly loaded? See our chapter on this. Does the weight exceed the maximum limits for the altitude and temperature of the field?
(e) Watch the distances on private fields. Are they sufficiently accurate for the aircraft, or is the operation near the limits which are not entirely reliable anyhow? Are the distances in feet or metres?
(f) Is the route planned so that a single-engine aircraft can reach a suitable emergency area, gliding with engine out?
(g) However many engines the aircraft has, is the ceiling checked, and then the terrain checked?

Operations from Runways contaminated with snow, slush or water. Avoid if possible: better to wait for clearance, or divert, rather than land on a contaminated runway.

3 mm of water, slush or wet snow
10 mm of dry snow
have a significant effect on performance – drag, power loss due to spray, poorer wheel braking, possibility of aquaplaning, less directional control.

Take-off. It's the condition of the upwind half of the runway that's important, where speeds are greatest. Isolated puddles of standing water are not significant, extensive areas are, and take-off should not be attempted if there is any doubt about depth.
Knowing this,
15 mm of water, slush, wet snow
60 mm of dry snow
are the absolute limits for take-off. Expect to take longer to unstick, use maximum take-off power available, and normal rotation and safety speeds. Never go in crosswinds of 10 kt or more, or with a tail wind.

In such conditions, marker boards (and the visibility must be good enough for them to be seen) are placed at 40% of the **Emergency distance available.** If the pilot is not at $\cdot85V_2$ by then, abandon the take-off, and don't assume any performance credit to a sloping runway or headwinds reported to be 10 kt or more when working out the take-off distance required.

Landing. Aquaplaning is likely with over 3 mm of standing water or slush over most of the runway: loss of directional control and negligible wheel-braking are a consequence. Once it's started, aquaplaning can continue in lesser depths, so make sure, if you've got to land in these conditions, that there is a big margin over the normal landing distance required, and there's no crosswind: if 'you've got to land', be very cagey indeed, in other words.

Wet runways
Terms used are:
(a) Damp – variations in runway surface colour due to moisture.
(b) Wet – runway surface soaked but no sign of standing water.
(c) Water patches – significant patches of standing water visible.
(d) Flooded – Extensive water patches visible.
If (c) or (d) reported, runway contamination should be assumed.

15: Playing safe

If you're flying so low as to be able to see the price of oranges in the market place, you're breaking the law, and you don't need us to tell you so. The avoidance of turning yourself into an aerial criminal (quite inadvertently) is another matter. When a distinguished lawyer gives a lecture on the legal and insurance aspects of private flying to a body as august as the Royal Aeronautical Society, there must be something in it for you, worthy of your close attention. So stay with us; this chapter won't help you in your examinations, but obedience to its precepts will emphatically keep you out of trouble – to some degree anyway.

A few general observations are worth mentioning in the first place. They are drawn from various statistics concerning prosecutions for breaches of the Air Navigation Order and the Rules of the Air – offences ranging from aerobatics over a congested area, to failure to enter the required particulars in a flying log book.

(i) The private pilot appears to be vulnerable, since professionals are rigorously inspected; but since there are no records of the number of hours flown annually by private pilots, a comparison of value on the incidence of reports against private and professional pilots cannot really be made.
(ii) There is no evidence of a vendetta against private pilots.
(iii) Very few of the reports against pilots come from the public – they're nearly all from the authorities.
(iv) There are too many complicated regulations which are difficult to interpret.

In the second place, further deductions could be made from a detailed study of the many cases examined:

(i) The number of PPL holders in the UK is around the 20 000 mark, and the punishment on conviction by a fine of the few irresponsible ones is scarcely salutary. Their licences should be withdrawn – there is power to do this under the Order, but since there is no machinery for appeal, it is rarely invoked.
(ii) The pilot has the responsibility of renewing his licences and certificates of airworthiness. The holder of a dog licence used to be reminded when to renew it, so we're told, but certainly a pilot must remind himself – and with a long period of licence validity, it is easy to forget to have a medical.
(iii) The pilots most to be feared are those who fail to flight plan with the necessary care, or who undertake flights for which they are not qualified; their suicidal tendencies involve them in activities which cause the most trouble to all and sundry.

(iv) Low flying charges are mostly based on poor evidence and are reasonably likely to fail if care is taken in the defence. Very few pilots deliberately low fly, it seems. A pilot flying at a precise height of 1 500 ft will be reported by ground observers to be at heights varying from 500 ft to 1 000 ft, and even experienced professional pilots among the observers have been proved well out in their estimates.

(v) Fines imposed by magistrates up and down the country vary considerably for similar offences. Benches have little experience of aviation matters, and there may even be residual resentment among them at the dash of the magnificent men in their flying machines who stole the birds from the pongoes during the war!

Far more important than warning pilots of the risk of being prosecuted is the need for pilots to realise the risks they run insofar as their insurances are concerned if they have an accident while committing a breach of the legislation. Nearly all policies of aviation insurance provide that breaking the law entitles the underwriter to repudiate liability if there is an accident. Since there is no compulsory third party insurance in aviation law, a crash on a house by a low flying pilot could result in financial disaster for both pilot and house owner. Makes you think, doesn't it?

Having said all this, and with an underlying sympathy for the problems besetting the private pilot, let's consider the rules to be followed for staying out of legal and insurance trouble. Counsels of perfection, the Royal Aeronautical Society lecturer called them, with a legal bearing.

(i) Have a current licence.

(ii) See that your aircraft has a current C of A and that the purpose of your flight does not conflict with any of its conditions; this applies even to a club aircraft.

(iii) See that your aircraft is properly covered for all aviation risks; this applies even to a club aircraft.

(iv) Do not deliberately fly low or engage in aerobatics over a built-up area. In particular, the 500 ft minimum rule should be remembered – and you don't need reminding that your altimeter is unlikely to be reading your height above the ground.

(v) Plan your flight if you are doing more than local flying, and do not violate controlled airspace.

(vi) Do not undertake more than you are technically capable of performing. The records show that the main causes of accidents to private pilots are the inadvertent stall and what is loosely called 'weather causes'. It is, therefore, of vital importance to take into account not only your own ability but also the performance capability of your aircraft. Familiarise yourself with its performance in the pilot's notes, or in the performance schedule which may form part of the C of A. En route safety can be achieved by a carefully prepared flight plan, taking advantage of all facilities, and having alternate plans if adverse weather is encountered. Do not forget that failure to ensure that a flight can safely be made is an offence under the Order.

(vii) Do not fly when you are ill, medicated, over-tired, depressed or angry. Testing flying conditions always seem to happen when you're feeling below par, anyway.

To the above, we would like to add our twopenn'orth: matters which have come to our attention since the publication of the aforementioned lecture in the Aeronautical Journal. When going on a flight, book out with details of route and expected flight time, naming the destination and alternate if landing away from base. This takes no time at all and, if landing away, it's worth the trouble of ringing back on safe arrival – and promising to do so – then, if overdue, the wheels can be set in motion to find you. Recently, a private aircraft went down on land 16 miles from the departure airfield in the South of England, and was not found for 9 weeks. Our second point is to enjoin you to study carefully the aircraft handbook. If an advert says, for example, that your aircraft has seats for 4 people and space for 200 lb of baggage, that does not mean that it will fly with 4 people **and** 200 lb of baggage. The aircraft handbook will set out all the facts.

And what's the score if you are reported for an offence? There are a few points in the procedure which it is worthwhile for a pilot to follow. Suppose you have been reported for low flying by a farmer while you were practising a forced landing exercise away from the aerodrome area. The report will have been made either to the local police or direct to the Civil Aviation Authority.

(i) If you were flying 500 ft, plead guilty and have done with it.

(ii) If it appears that an offence has been committed, statements will be sought from those who reported the offence and, if possible, from you. Six months can elapse before information is laid before the magistrates by the police, so a pilot may not be aware for some months that he's been reported; and if he does know, may think it's been allowed to lapse.

(iii) When the air legislation investigation branch seeks to get a statement from you, don't make one without consulting a solicitor; and have the solicitor present at the interview. You do not have to make a statement, and it is usually unwise to do so. It is better to have your evidence brought out in court by your counsel if a prosecution ensues. But a police officer may question you, though he must caution you; then you must be quite sure that any statement you make is correct, for it can be used in evidence, and cannot be withdrawn. Make sure, too, that you get a copy.

(iv) If a prosecution is to follow, you will be served with a summons. Then, with the help of your solicitor a full statement will be prepared, giving charts of the area, an aftercast of the weather and statements from your passenger if carried. Ask for an adjournment if you need more time to prepare your defence than the summons permits.

(v) Engage an expert in aviation matters; his qualifications will be vital to your case. He will testify upon the difficulty of judging the height of passing aircraft, the colour and cloud cover of the sky, the size and colouring of the aircraft, the size and noise of the engine, the absence of visual references. This evidence should be sufficient, with the skilful cross-examination of witnesses, to indicate how unlikely it is that you were flying below 500 ft if you are certain (and prepared to swear) that you were not.

(vi) If you win, you may get an award for costs; you may be sure that the award will not by any means cover your actual disbursements.

(vii) If you lose, you may have to pay the costs of the prosecution, your fine, as well as your own costs!

(viii) You can appeal in a suitable case and will be advised of your chances, but it is worthy of note that a prosecution is unlikely in the first place unless it is reasonably sure of succeeding.

This sounds very expensive, arduous and depressing, but there is no evidence that the law is over-rigorously applied. Flagrant breaches are fairly easy to avoid, and minor inadvertent breaches must be avoided by personal organisation. Systematic checks – of insurance matters, too – must be made before you even think of taking to the air.

16: Getting a PPL from scratch

As much of this book is devoted to clarifying rules, regulations and restrictions which surround the qualified private pilot, it seems sensible to line up the procedures and requirements which are demanded of anyone who decides to take some practical steps towards becoming a pilot. The full story is given in 'The Private Pilot's Licence', known as CAP 53, and the privileges are set out in The Air Navigation Order, 1985. Both are issued by HMSO. We will now attempt to summarise these documents in clear bell-like tones, omitting only those refinements and corollaries without which no official ukase would be complete.

The first thing is to visit a local flying club, preferably on a sunny weekend when there's plenty of activity, to get the general feeling of enthusiasm and efficiency; this shows through remarkably quickly to the keen observer. The quality and appearance of the aircraft in the hangar are useful indications, too, of a Club's standards. Don't be put off by the bars and lounge, though; it seems traditional to preserve these at poor transport cafe level. Whatever happens, your time won't be wasted; flying clubs always get a high quota of attractive birds, nearly as good as the pits at Silverstone.

Most clubs offer a trial lesson, at barely cost price and it's well worth the price if you've never been airborne in a light aircraft. It's a trip of about half an hour with a qualified pilot/instructor, and he'll give you a feel of the controls. The flight will either increase your urge to become a pilot or make you shoot the cat; and in the latter event, you will be saved a lot of time, money and disappointment. Incidentally, there's no relationship between sea-sickness and air-sickness; there are numberless pilots who never feel a qualm in the air but wouldn't dream of taking the Isle of Wight ferry.

It's not yet time to join the club of your choice, for to be allowed the privilege of being instructed you must be 17 and fit enough to fly, so a **medical examination** must be passed, conducted by an approved doctor (a list of those in the locality is kept at the club or can be obtained from the Aircraft Owners and Pilots Association, 50a Cambridge Street, London SW1V 4QQ). We daren't quote a fee; you cough up on the spot; you'll have coughed once or twice during the examination, anyway, if you're a boy. Perish the thought that there is anything perfunctory about this medical; you will be given a good going over; spectacles, by the way, are quite permissible. **The Medical Certificate** granted after a successful exam is your licence to fly. It is valid for 5 years if you are under 40; 2 years if you're between 40 and 50 and 6 months if you are over 70 on the date of issue, the ravages of time and gin being considered to accelerate the deterioration of the body's faculties.

This Medical Certificate allows you to fly in command in order to qualify for a pilot's licence, but you cannot be in command with another person on board; every flight must be carried out in accordance with the instructions of a licensed pilot who has an Instructor's rating; the privileges are restricted to the UK, unless another area is specified on the certificate.

With this Medical Certificate in hand, the way is now clear to take a course in flying and gentle technical study to obtain a **Private Pilot's Licence.** The Medical Certificate will be transferred to your PPL unless 13 months has passed since your last medical, in which case you're under the doctor again; if 6 months has passed, you have to declare you're still fit. Now is the time to approach the Chief Instructor at your club with a view to joining and signing on for the course. You will have to get past the receptionist first, usually a highly nubile young lady who will lead you to the flying instructor she thinks you deserve, often depending on the place that instructor has in her affections at the time. Better to ask for an interview with the CFI, who will take a professional attitude to your application.

Once accepted for the course, buy a log book, a sacred document, my goodness. The club will sell you one, or HMSO (Personal Flying Log Book, form 24), and in it you must inscribe in a fair round hand in ink or indelible pencil the details of every flight you make; your instructor will advise you in full. As it will eventually and frequently make its way to the CCA in support of licence applications and renewals, it must be most carefully kept, and officially stamped and signed by or on behalf of the CFI whenever required in support of such applications.

Your flying instructor will give you flying lessons and you need technical instruction for the written exams, and clubs arrange lectures and discussions for their members in addition. The course of flying involves 43 hours as a pilot, though it is reduced to 38 hours if you run the course steadily at the same club, and that course is approved. The choice gives some freedom of action to the chap whose business takes him about the country, and must take his lessons where he finds them. Such a one has scarcely any limit to the time he takes to get his 43 hours, but to qualify for the reduction to 38 hours all the requirements must be completed in 6 months – this can be very tough going. Of the hours of flying experience demanded, 10 hours must be as pilot in command. In the 10 hours, 4 hours cross-country flying must be included with two intermediate stops on one flight, one of them 50 nm from the departure field. This cross-country flying must be done in the 6 months preceding the application for the licence. Finally, adequate dual instruction under a qualified instructor – and adequate is construed as 20 hours.

When you've done your hours, and feel ready to have a go at the flying test and ground examinations, you may arrange these with an authorised examiner at the club or in the locality; or you may apply to the CAA (not entirely to be recommended, as the written exams are held in London, the flying test at Stansted in Essex, and you must send in application forms, your log book, the requisite fees, and wait for the call). At your own club, you can take the flying test and technical exams by mutual arrangement, and it's the examiner who parcels up your application forms, results, log book and cheque, using your postage stamp, and sends if off to CAA, FCL3 again. A Certificate of Test will be entered in the applicant's Log Book by the CAA. The tests and ground examinations must all be passed within the 6 months preceding the date of issue of the PPL, and although this is easier than doing all the training as well in this time, it can reach panic stations if you, say, pip one of the requirements and have to undergo further training before having another go at the test, especially in winter.

The licence is valid permanently now, and consists of a fine old packet of cardboard in a plastic wallet:

(1) A basic Licence and Aircraft Rating card.
(2) Individual Rating cards for the IMC, Instrument Night, Assistant Flying Instructor and Flying Instructor Rating.
(3) A card for the R/T Licence.
(4) The Medical Certificate as issued.

The Medical Certificate must be current, of course, but every 13 months the 'privileges attached to the licence' must be renewed by submitting your log book to the authorised examiner, who will issue a Certificate of Experience, i.e. keep the licence valid, if he's satisfied you have managed the requisite flying, as a pilot in command, during that 13 months; 5 hours flying is required in aircraft of the Group noted in the licence. The Certificate of Experience will be stamped in your log book by the examiner, using a rubber stamp issued by the CAA.

If the licence lapses at this stage, then another flight test must be taken. If successful, the Certificate of test will be stamped in your log book by the examiner, with the official rubber stamp.

Should you wish to extend your licence to another Group of aircraft, a flying test must be taken on the new type; so it is possible to have a PPL for some sizeable aeroplanes. The initial Certificate of Test for a new rating will be stamped in your log book by the CAA. And if you've not flown as a pilot in command for 26 months, you'll have to undergo further training and pass a flight test in order to renew the aircraft rating of the licence.

As well as all that, the medical looms largely, of course, and one must be taken and passed every 5 years if you are under 40 and every 2 years once that ripe old age is attained. There is one redeeming feature about renewal medicals, however, in that the certificate is issued for inclusion in the licence on the spot, so take your licence and most recent medical certificate with you to the doctor. Keeping your licence up to date, together with your medical certificate without which it is invalid, is entirely the responsibility of the pilot, for no reminders are issued.

The privileges of a PPL allow the holder to fly in command of any of the aircraft types specified on the licence, but he must never engage in public transport or aerial work, or accept any remuneration for flying except when giving instruction to a fellow club member in a club aircraft. He must not fly outside controlled airspace when the flight visibility is less than 1·5 nm; he must not carry any passenger above 3 000 ft amsl in IMC, nor at or below 3 000 ft amsl in a flight visibility of less than 3 nm; he must not fly on special VFR in a control zone in a flight visibility of less than 5 nm, except in a traffic zone or route specifically notified as exempt from this proviso. He must not fly at night with a passenger unless he's got a night rating **and** an instrument rating, or has, within the preceding 6 months, carried out 5 take-offs and 5 landings when the centre of the Sun is depressed at least 12° below the horizon – a pedantic way of saying it's absolute darkness. All these provisions assume you are in command, and if you care to read them again, you will find there is plenty of scope to spread your wings. Perhaps a futher study of the chapter entitled 'Playing Safe' would be wise, now.

Navigation equipment, charts, etc

You don't need a lot, and its worth the few extra bob to get the best. Run a mile from any chum who offers you his old computer, even if it's for freeness; it will seize up in the middle of your examination, we've seen it happen.

The gear is obtainable from many shops that cater for draughtsmen, but the specialist airmen's shops are naturally the places to browse around it you've got the time, and most clubs keep the usual equipment handy. Airtour International has a place at Elstree Aerodrome, Elstree, Herts, and supplies many clubs. AOPA (Aircraft Owners and Pilots Association), 50a Cambridge Street, London SW1, keep a goodly stock.

Computer: are manifold in design, complexity and ruggedness. Make certain you get one with freely moving circles on both sides; that the slide goes up to at least 700 kt; that the circular slide rule is really comprehensive (all the conversions, ft, m, gal, km, litres, etc., Mach number, specific gravity, a high range of temperature in the airspeed window), and beware of movable wind arms on the face. Jeppesen, Aristo are good; Airtour's own model, though plastic, has proved serviceable and it's got the lot. And is one of the least expensive.

Protractor: buy a Douglas, preferably with 'N' marked solid or in red, of pliable material; the thicker type is inclined to break.

Dividers: the compass-divider type is best, fairly stiff.

Maps: topographical maps will depend on your flying area. They are surely available at your aerodrome, but are supplied by:

Edward Stanford, Ltd, 12–14 Long Acre, London, WC2.

We've referred in the text to ICAO 1:500 000 Southern England and Wales.

Aeronautical Information Circulars are available from the Aeronautical Information Service, Tolcarne Drive, Pinner, Middlesex HA5 2DU. Just put your name on their list. The circular on aviation charts is a useful one, as it lists the conventional signs and symbols.

Aerad charts are available from Airtour's shops, address above, and at many aerodromes; they do go out of date rather quickly. We have referred in the text to EUR 1/2.

We've not quoted any prices as it would be pointless.

Abbreviations

A/c, a/c	aircraft
Ac	altocumulus
ADF	automatic direction finder
ADR	advisory route
AFISO	Aerodrome Flight Information Service Officer
AFTN	Aeronautical Fixed Telecommunication Network
agl	above ground level
A/H	alter Heading
AIS	Aeronautical Information Service
alt or Alt	altitude
amsl	above mean sea level
ANO	Air Navigation Order, 1985
As	altostratus
ASA	Advisory Service Area
ASI	airspeed indicator
ASR	Altimeter Setting Region
ATA	actual time of arrival
ATC	Air Traffic Control
ATCC	Air Traffic Control Centre
ATCU	Air Traffic Control Unit
ATD	actual time of departure
ATIS	Automatic Terminal Information Service
ATS	Air Traffic Service
ATSU	Air Traffic Service Unit
ATZ	Aerodrome Traffic Zone
AUW	all-up weight
BFO	beat frequency oscillator
Brg	bearing
°C	degrees Celsius (formerly Centigrade)
°(C)	degrees Compass
CAA	Civil Aviation Authority
CAVOK	weather fine and clear (in general terms)
Cb	cumulonimbus
Cc	cirrocumulus
C of A	Certificate of Airworthiness
ch lat	change of latitude
ch long	change of longitude
Ci	cirrus
C of G or CG	centre of gravity
C/S or c/s	callsign
Cs	cirrostratus

CTR	Control Zone
CW	carrier wave
Cu	cumulus
DALR	dry adiabatic lapse rate
Dev	Deviation
DF	direction finding
DGI	directional gyro indicator
DME	distance measuring equipment
DR	dead reckoning
EAT	estimated approach time
ELR	environmental lapse rate
ETA	estimated time of arrival
ETD	estimated time of departure
FIR	Flight Information Region
FIS	Flight Information Service
FL	Flight Level
ft/min	feet per minute
gal/hr	gallons per hour
GC	great circle
GD	Greenwich date
GMT	Greenwich Mean Time
G/S	ground speed
Hdg	Heading
HF	high frequency
HHI	horizontal hard iron
ht	height
Hz	hertz (i.e. cycles per second)
IAS	indicated airspeed
ICAO	International Civil Aviation Organisation
ident	identification
IFR	Instrument Flight Rules
ILS	Instrument Landing System
IMC	Instrument Meteorological Conditions
ISA	international standard atmosphere
kg	kilogram(s)
kg/hr	kilograms per hour
kHz	1 000 Hz
km/hr	kilometres per hour
kt	knot(s)
Lat	Latitude
lb/hr	pounds per hour
Ldg wt	landing weight
Long	Longitude
°(M)	degrees Magnetic
MATZ	Military Aerodrome Traffic Zone
mb	millibar(s)
MF	medium frequency

MHz	megahertz
min	minute(s)
mm	millimetre(s)
MoD	Ministry of Defence
MM	middle marker
msl	mean sea level
NATS	National Air Traffic Services
NDB	non-directional beacon
NH	northern hemisphere
nm	nautical mile(s)
NP	North Pole
Ns	nimbostratus
OBS	Omni-bearing Selector
OCL	obstacle clearance limit
OM	outer marker
Order	Air Navigation Order, 1985
O/R	on request
PE	pressure error
posn	position
PP	pinpoint
PPO	prior permission only
press alt	pressure altitude
QFE, QFF,	
QNE, QNH	are defined in the text (see pages 124 and 125)
RAS	rectified airspeed
RB	relative bearing
RCC	Rescue Co-ordination Centre
Regs	Regulations
RL	rhumb line
RMI	Radio Magnetic Indicator
RNLI	Royal National Lifeboat Institution
rpm	revolutions per minute
R/T	radio telephony
RVR	Runway Visual Range
R/W	Runway
Rx	receiver
SALR	saturated adiabatic lapse rate
Sc	stratocumulus
S & R	Search and Rescue
Sch	Schedule
SH	southern hemisphere
S/H	set Heading
sm	statute mile(s)
SP	South Pole
S/R	sunrise
SRZ	Special Rules Zone
S/S	sunset

Stn	station
St	stratus
°(T)	degrees True
TAS	True airspeed
TB	True bearing
TE	Track error
TMA	Terminal Control Area
TMG	Track made good
TN	True North
T/O	take-off
TOC	top of climb
TOW	take-off weight
Tr	Track
Trans Alt	Transition Altitude
Trans Lev	Transition Level
Tx	Transmitter
UIR	Upper Flight Information Region
UK	United Kingdom
UKAP	United Kingdom Aeronautical Information Publication known as the UK Air Pilot
u/s	unserviceable
Var	Variation
VDF	VHF Direction Finding
VFR	Visual Flight Rules
VHF	very high frequency
VIP	very important person
vis	visibility
VMC	Visual Meteorological Conditions
VOR	very high frequency omni-directional range
VSI	vertical soft iron
W/D	wind direction
wind comp	wind component
W/E	wind effect
W/S	wind speed
wt	weight
W/V	wind velocity

Index